DIRTY DEEDS

MARK EVANS

DIRTY DEEDS

My life inside and outside of AC/DC

ALLEN & UNWIN

This edition published in 2012
First published in 2011

Allen & Unwin
Sydney, Melbourne, Auckland, London

83 Alexander Street
Crows Nest NSW 2065
Australia
Phone: (61 2) 8425 0100
Fax: (61 2) 9906 2218
Email: info@allenandunwin.com
Web: www.allenandunwin.com

Cataloguing-in-Publication details are available
from the National Library of Australia
www.trove.nla.gov.au

ISBN 978 1 74331 084 7

Internal design by Post Pre-press Group, Australia
Set in Utopia by Post Pre-press Group, Australia

10 9 8 7 6 5 4 3

For My Girls

Prologue

Paris, April 1977

Ever since I could remember I'd wanted to travel. I didn't quite recognise it as travel at the time, of course, but I was aware very early on that there was a lot of stuff out there to see and experience. Some of my first memories are of painting pictures of what I thought to be far-off, historical, often mysterious places: the Pyramids, Big Ben and even the Sydney Harbour Bridge. (Hey, I was from Melbourne; Sydney seemed like another world to me.) I was intrigued by the notion that there were countries on the other side of the world and that the people there spoke different languages, ate different food, wore different clothes, and were just so . . . different. There seemed to be one major problem, though; just how did I get to these far-off, wonderfully different places? I was from a working-class family, raised on a rough-and-ready housing commission estate in suburban Prahran. What chance did I stand of travelling the world?

The answer lay in becoming the bass player in AC/DC.

Thanks to a tip-off from a buddy of mine, I joined the band in Melbourne in March 1975. I had just turned nineteen. We gigged, toured, recorded, drank and basically caroused our way across Australia during my first year on board. We'd achieved very healthy chart success and earned the ire of parts of the establishment, which prompted us to dub a tour 'Lock Up Your Daughters'. When that run ended it was deemed a damned good idea to do exactly the same through the UK and Europe. And away we went.

By 5 April 1977 we found ourselves in Paris, on the fag end of a European tour supporting the Ozzy Osbourne-led Black Sabbath. The gig that night had been at the Pavillion de Paris, which was not dissimilar to our old haunt in Sydney, the Hordern Pavilion. The Paris Pavillion had the added attraction of being on the site of an old slaughterhouse, so the venue was known locally as Les Abattoirs. I had no doubt the place suffered a serious hangover from its gory and inglorious past. It smelled exactly as you would imagine a former Parisian slaughterhouse to smell, except for one thing—it was much, much worse.

But the city itself was another story. Paris in the springtime is a fantastic place. If there isn't already a song with the title 'Paris in the Springtime', I want to know why. And it was an exciting place for a bunch of young guys in a rock and roll band. When I say 'young', I am referring to the players in AC/DC, not our beloved and fearless social director and singer, Bon Scott. He was known to one and all as the 'old man' and it was a bit like (no, it was very much like) having your slightly crazed uncle on the road with you. You know the one; he gets outrageously pissed at weddings and tries it on with all the young lassies. Bon was all of thirty, but to me he was a relic from a past generation.

Paris being Paris and AC/DC being AC/DC, we were all giving it a good going-over during our stay, except for, on all but very rare occasions, Angus Young, a teetotalling guitarist in schoolboy uniform. As for the old man, Bon was keen on a drop of red, sometimes substantially more than a drop. And Paris was just the place to get plastered on a robust red. During this visit Bon and I had lucked out—we were keeping company and rubbing shoulders (along with other parts of our bodies) with two very attractive French girls. We had spent a couple of hectic days and nights in their company and decided to repair back to our hotel off the Boulevard Saint-Germain with our dear new French friends after the Pavillion gig.

Parisian hotels are, shall we say, compact at best. More often than not they feature these tiny little balconies, with barely enough room for two people—two small people at that. Bon and I were shellacked but sharing yet another bottle of red on the tiny balcony, watching the sun come up over the City of Light. Paris looks absolutely magnificent at dawn, probably not much different from how it would have appeared a hundred years before, or even more. I could understand why the city had been such an inspiration for writers, painters, musicians and the rest. It seemed like time had been suspended.

So Bon and I were on our balcony, sipping away, feeling more than a little pleased with ourselves and our *deux filles Parisiennes très attirantes*. We were well and truly lit up and savouring a stunning Parisian sunrise. Life was good. I'd come a long way from Prahran—and in a pretty short time.

As I was having a serious gloat to Bon, who was somewhat the worse for wear after two days on the turps, he stared fixedly at the Eiffel Tower with an odd look on his face.

'What's up, mate?' I asked him.

Slowly, Bon turned to me. 'You know,' he said, 'there's a tower just like that in Paris.'

Chapter 1

The Prahran Hilton

I was raised in what would now be called a 'blended family', not that I minded or even cared. I was the youngest of a family of four kids—my eldest sister Laura and my brother John are from my father's first marriage to a beautiful woman named Susan, who died of a brain haemorrhage when they were very young. I vividly recall seeing a portrait of Susan in our home in the Melbourne suburb of Murrumbeena and thinking she was a movie star. Whenever I see that photo in my brother's home, I'm immediately back in our old place, all those years ago. It's a truly warm feeling and it's a time I miss immensely.

My other sister, Judy, who is five years older than me and the closest in age, was from my mother Norma's first marriage. Being the youngest, I was doted on and spoiled and probably made Judy's life hell, for which I now apologise. My mother's first husband, Bub Mintovich, was born in Australia to Russian Jewish parents. He was serving in the

Royal Australian Navy when they were married; he and my mother were only nineteen. They had been married for only two months, and Mum was pregnant with Judy, when Bub sailed for Okinawa aboard the HMAS *Bataan*. The *Bataan* was docked at Okinawa when the Korean War broke out on 25 June 1950, and the ship was then attached to the US Navy. Bub wouldn't return home for fifteen months. During that time he was part of the landing of United Nations troops at Pohang-dong, patrolled the Korean Straits, was involved in numerous blockades and bombardments, and came under fire on a daily basis.

Bub returned a much-changed man. Warfare had clearly taken its toll. He was stressed and withdrawn, barely twenty-one but with a ten-month-old daughter and living with his in-laws. When the chance came for Bub to move his new family to Darwin with the navy, my grandfather, Will, flatly refused to let my mother and sister leave, and the marriage broke down. What brightened the place up at that time was the presence of a couple of kids from the next street, a nine-year-old boy and thirteen-year-old girl, who would visit on a daily basis to see 'Mr and Mrs Whit' and the baby. The kids needed some light too; Laura and John had just lost their mother, Susan. Although strictly speaking my siblings are a half-brother and two half-sisters, I've never thought of them as anything other than my brother and sisters. They're my family; it's as simple as that.

I reckon it's fairly safe to say that my upbringing was a little challenging. I spent a lot of my youth in flat 56 of a housing project named the Horace Petty Estate in South Yarra. It was a pretty grand name for a dump. To me it will always be the Prahran Hilton—or Club 56, as my mates dubbed it. The

Horace Petty Estate comprised three twelve-storey blocks of flats and around thirty or so four-storey blocks. These were all prefabricated concrete constructions, bolted together like packs of cards. It was stinking hot in summer and in winter it was like living in a massive esky. After a stifling December day you might be lucky and have a cool change blow in, but as the concrete slabs started to cool they'd contract and start shifting. This was followed by a groaning noise and the occasional crack. It wasn't real comforting if you were living anywhere above the ground floor.

I once read a newspaper article about the Housing Commission projects, complete with a photo of the Hilton taken from the air. The title of the article was THE HORACE PETTY ESTATE ... A SOCIAL EXPERIMENT GONE WRONG. Thanks very much!

The move to Prahran from Murrumbeena seemed like great news for our family. Our house in Murrumbeena, while not a complete dump, was rundown; it lacked basic creature comforts like hot water, carpet and an inside toilet. It was cheap, though, which was about the only thing going for it. John and I shared an enclosed first-floor sunroom which looked out over Murrumbeena Road, towards the railway station. At night, our room was lit by a giant polar bear advertising Sennett's Ice Cream that resided on the awning outside my window. I used to listen to it hum and crackle as I drifted off to sleep.

Come winter it was appropriate that there was a polar bear living outside my bedroom window; our house felt like the North Pole in the winter months. I'd be lying there in bed, shivering, wearing pyjamas, footy socks, footy jumper, beanie, the works, with that smartarse polar bear happily humming away outside. After particularly bitter nights I would wake up numb from the knees down, my hands aching like crazy.

My family had fallen on hard times. My father was having trouble finding work. He'd lost his salesman job at Patterson's Furniture on Chapel Street, Prahran. He had been charged with assaulting a cop, who wound up with a broken arm and jaw, lacerations and bite marks on his butt. This was not from my dad, mind you, but courtesy of our trusty family dog, Chris.

My brother John had been with two pals at our local milk bar (the one with the polar bear on top) when the policeman told them to move on. One thing led to another and the policeman started hitting John's head against a brick wall. At that moment my father and Chris came around the corner, which spelled bad timing for the copper. The local busybody saw it all and made a statement, Dad was arrested and ended up on the front pages of the Melbourne papers. It came to the attention of Sir Maurice Nathan, the chairman of Patterson's. Dad was sacked immediately; 'he was not fit to be seen by the public'.

My father, John and his two friends were all charged with the assault—Chris the dog got off—and went to trial. On the advice of a well-heeled friend we engaged Sir Frank Galbally, the top criminal lawyer of the day. They were found guilty, fined heavily and received two-year good-behaviour bonds. The defence was a huge expense but thankfully their benefactor paid all costs and fines.

This was when we moved a few suburbs north. Our brand-new three-bedroom apartment was on the fourth floor of a 'walk-up' in South Yarra. It came complete with hot water and heating, and Dad arranged for some carpet and new furniture, which gave us the feeling of upward mobility. All we needed was a phone to complete our ascent, but Dad was unmovable on that one. 'They can come knock on the door if they want to talk to us,' he said. Just who 'they' were was never made plain, but I'm sure you get what he was telling us.

The fact that our address was South Yarra and not Prahran was a big deal. South Yarra was (and is) an extremely affluent area of Melbourne, but our new home, the Horace Petty Estate, was squeezed into a crap corner of it. If people asked where you were from and you told them South Yarra, you were almost certainly a toff, but once they realised you were from 'the flats' you were definitely right back there on Shit Street.

Just around the corner from our place was the Harold Holt Memorial Swimming Pool, another unfortunately named spot, given that in 1967 the then PM jumped in the drink and never came back.

When we moved, I decided I wanted to stay at the same school, Murrumbeena State School. My folks heard me out and said that if I was prepared to do all the travelling by myself, it was okay. Plus, I could walk to the station each morning with Dad, just the two of us, and talk. Unfortunately that didn't last long because his health was failing, and although he'd found work on the night shift at Repco Auto Parts, and then in the furniture department—of all places—at Foys in the city, he had to stop work not long after. I caught the train from Hawksburn Station, sat out six stops and then walked up Hobart Road to school. I did this for half of fifth grade and all of sixth. Rail travel came with an added bonus. I was befriended by two pretty teenage girls at Hawksburn Station, who attended the MLC school at Caulfield. They insisted I sit in between them and cuddle all the way to Caulfield. I offered no resistance.

Murrumbeena State School was the absolute opposite of the Horace Petty Estate. No one swore, spat or thought about punching or kicking anyone or anything. No one was ever sent out of class, or got kept behind after school. We even had our own swimming pool in the schoolyard, plus two football fields. I couldn't have asked for more. I led two lives: an ordered, disciplined one at Murrumbeena State and a chaotic, tribal, *Lord of the Flies* existence at the Prahran Hilton, with my only sanctuary up on the fourth floor.

I was an average student. I never stood out academically but I didn't get into trouble, either. I lived to play footy, and played all year round. From second grade on, the top ten per cent of each class were given an Honour Certificate to reward their performance. I wasn't even close in years two, three and four, and then I started missing days regularly in fifth and sixth grade to help care for Dad, so I did my schoolwork at home. My marks actually went up and I got Honour Certificates in those years. I came third overall in my sixth-grade class.

While I don't think too poorly of the Hilton, it took some getting used to. I was ten years old when we moved in and we hadn't been there for long when I was beaten up every night for a week as I walked home across the estate from Hawksburn railway station. My injuries weren't serious, although I did need a few trips to the Alfred Hospital for a broken nose and to get a few stitches. It was becoming a bit of a regular thing when my dad pulled me up and said: 'How long are you going to put up with this?' I had put in a few playful spars with

Dad and my brother John, a good boxer who later turned pro and took world champ featherweight Johnny Famechon the full ten rounds, only to lose on points. But I wasn't a fighter.

My usual assailants were a group of three: two brothers and their chubby mate. This kid was huge, and a couple of years older than me, a big thing when you're ten and scared. He was the one assigned to do me over the next time our paths crossed, but being much smaller and faster than him, I gave Fatty the slip. Which was great for me but not for him: as I scarpered his two so-called mates turned around and beat the tripe out of him. It was merciless. It's strange; I could handle being beaten up, but had some real issues with these guys beating the crap out of their 'friend'. So I turned around and yelled at them to quit it, which provoked the standard response: 'What are you going to do about it?' Tentatively, I walked back towards them and saw the guy on the ground. He was a real mess. There was blood everywhere and he was blubbering—he'd also pissed himself. As I got closer I discovered he'd shit himself, too. So there he was, beaten senseless, crying and marinating in his own piss and crap. Not a stellar day for the big guy.

I didn't have a plan and, frankly, was ready to shit myself, too. But I just had this feeling of pure rage, maybe for the first time in my life. Without thinking too much I dropped my school bag and took an almighty swing at the older of the two brothers. It was the first 'real' punch I'd thrown in my life. The punch, even if I say so myself, was a ripper, catching him flush on the chin. I think I was as stunned as he was, because he went down as if I'd hit him with a cricket bat. I have this memory of the guy falling straight back—all I saw were the whites of his eyes and him dropping. His brother took off like a shot, yelling, 'I'm getting my dad.' I wasn't far behind him, straight up the stairs and into our apartment.

Dad was there; he was home a lot in those days, although I didn't know exactly what was ailing him. What I did notice was the huge smile on his face—in fact, it's my warmest memory of him. Smiles were at a premium those days; I had a feeling he knew something was up regarding his immediate future. Dad reached over and ruffled my hair. 'Nice punch, mate.' He said I'd done the right thing, sticking up for someone in trouble. Dad had been watching me from the kitchen window and had willed me out loud to turn back and help. It was one of the last strong memories I have of my dad.

It's odd to look in the mirror and see my resemblance to him. It's a warm feeling. I know I have my father's smile; my sister Laura's eyes still well up if she sees me break into a grin. I have his olive skin tone; we'd both turn an identical colour if we'd been out in the sun. 'You'd get a tan if you slept with the light on, son.' I can hear him saying that now. I can still feel how good it was to get a hug from him, and how good it would feel if he surprised me and said: 'Take the day off from school, mate, let's go to the beach, just us.' I can also feel how those hugs lost their strength but never their warmth as he faded away from all of us.

My father was an interesting fellow. He was tough, an ex-boxer who trained my brother. He was hard and soft at the same time. He was also what some might call a 'colourful racing identity', and seemed to have friends all over the place, particularly in the Chinese community. My godfather was Chinese. When we'd go to watch our team Carlton play, we'd stop at one pub for lunch, another for a 'quick beer', and another, then another. I was amazed how friendly everyone was, and how we never seemed to pay for anything. 'Pat and his boys are here! What you having, young fella?' For me it was always a red lemonade and a packet of chips.

My mother told me how one evening early in their relationship she and Dad were on their way to visit my future godfather, who lived in Canning Street, North Melbourne. My father became aware that three men were following them. Dad greeted my godfather on his porch and called out to him, 'Which way to the station, mate? We're lost.' He got the directions, gave my mother a hug, placed something heavy into her coat pocket and took off for the station, simply saying: 'See you later.'

Dad crossed the street and the men followed. When Dad returned he was cut, battered and bruised. 'It would have been a lot worse if they had got the gun,' he told Mum.

Apparently Dad changed his ways not long after I was born. Mum had a massive nervous breakdown, was hospitalised for six months and endured many bouts of electroshock treatment. Dad was left with the four of us to care for. That's how he became a furniture salesman at Patterson's in Prahran.

Still, I didn't really know my father as well as I would have liked to, although what lessons I did learn from him are still with me. I was about as prepared as I could be for his passing because it was obvious it was a battle we weren't going to win, especially during the last six months of his life. I loved it when I'd come home from school and would go to my parents' room—Dad was bedridden by this time—and Mum's lipstick would be the only colour evident on my father's face.

He'd smile at me and say, 'Your mother's been at it again, Mark.'

It still makes me laugh, even though he didn't have the strength to wipe the lipstick off if he'd wanted to. It sums up my take on Dad. He was obviously in a lot of pain and trying to come to terms with his imminent departure but he still wanted to share a joke with me—at my mother's expense, of course. He was a relatively young man, virtually the same age I am now, and he knew he was dying. But he still wanted to make his son laugh in an atmosphere where laughs were hard to come by.

One afternoon in late March 1968, I'd been kicking the football with my mate Steven Kelly (who is my brother-in-law's brother . . . is there a specific name for that?). It was getting late and I was on my way back to our apartment when I saw my brother walking towards me. I knew this was it. He was married and not living with us; why else would he be here and look like that? I knew it was Dad and I started running. I went straight past my brother and into our block of flats.

Dad had been deteriorating for a month or so. His painkiller intake had been upped so he wasn't lucid much of the time, but we could still talk between the morphine backing off and the pain overtaking him. He was drifting away; we all knew it. He did his best to see visitors, but it was painful for everyone. It'd drive him nuts when friends would lose it. 'Go cry somewhere else—tell me a joke, or piss off,' he'd say when some old pal would start blubbering.

I used to sit with him. He looked like a skeleton with skin attached; he seemed to be shrinking, but his smile was still there and I could sometimes snatch a chat with him. I would set up my stuff on the bed and work away, fixing my Scalextric slot cars when he drifted off, and wait for him to come back. Eventually he would stir. 'Shit, are you still here?' he'd chuckle.

I know the rest of the family tried to shield me from the illness. I was only twelve but I wanted to spend time with Dad, help him if I could, even if it was just to get him to the toilet and clean him up. I knew it was getting near the end when he couldn't walk and needed a wheelchair. During those last couple of weeks I could lift him out of the chair with a bit of extra effort and onto the toilet. It felt good to be able to help, move his pillow, get him another ice cube to suck on, just do something to try to make him feel better. I'm not sure that kids get enough credit for being able to handle tragedy. I have the feeling, from my experience, that they have a great capacity to adapt to adverse conditions. Youngsters can breathe some much-needed fresh air into real shitty situations, purely through their honesty.

This day in late March, when I got to Dad's room, he was making some awful sounds. Mum was holding onto him, rocking him back and forth like you would a sick child. 'Don't go, Pat!' she was saying. Mum broke down completely when she saw me. It felt weird seeing Mum so upset. I went to go to her but she shooed me away and asked John to take me outside.

John and I stood on our balcony, overlooking the basketball court. He looked at me but all he could say was, 'Sorry, mate.' We stood there for a while. John had his arm round my shoulder. 'I'm going to see Dad, you stay here.' I could hear everything happening inside from my spot on the balcony. The awful noises were becoming less audible as Dad slipped further away and we waited for the ambulance. I was getting numb; it was confusing. I was listening to the noises but I would drift away, watching some friends play basketball on the court several floors below. Then a noise would drag me back. Where was the ambulance? Why was it taking so long to get here?

When the ambos did arrive, the lift was too small for the gurney, so Dad was strapped onto a stretcher, which had to be turned almost upright to get inside the lift. The ride down only took twenty seconds or so but it felt like an eternity; it's embedded in my memory forever. He was limp, sagging on the stretcher and his breathing was ragged. The lift floor was filthy and smelled of piss. Dad's feet were bare. I was worried his feet would get dirty, because he would hate that. He'd never go anywhere barefoot.

He was loaded into the ambulance with Mum and John while I looked on. All his noises had stopped. I was sure he was gone. It was very, very quiet, except for the slap, slap, slap of the ball being dribbled down the concrete basketball court across the car park. I rode the stinking lift up to the apartment and sat alone in my room. Dad died on 22 March 1968.

I still miss my father; in fact I miss him more as the years pass. There is just so much I would have liked to share with him but didn't get the chance. Dad, John and I did, however, share a love of the Carlton Football Club, the Mighty Blues. I cherish the memory of watching the Blues at Princes Park from atop Dad's shoulders, eating fresh peanuts and picking the shells out of his thick, black, Brylcreemed hair. I'd cry when the Blues copped yet another belting, but Dad would comfort me, saying: 'There's always next week, son.' I tried not to cry in front of John when, six months after Dad died, the Blues finally won the 1968 Grand Final. I turned to John, to see him absolutely drowning in a sea of tears. I yelled to the sky: 'I TOLD YOU WE'D DO IT!'

All through sixth grade at Murrumbeena State School, I'd take Fridays off to stay home and spend some time with Dad. In 1967, just before Christmas, I remember telling him that I didn't want to go to his funeral.

'That's all right,' he said. 'You don't have to go if you don't want to.'

My god—how must he have felt? My blood runs cold when I think of one of my kids saying that. I didn't go to his funeral and it's probably the reason I still struggle with those memories. I carried a lot of guilt around for quite some time about not going. I still have dreams where my father pops up and says, 'I didn't expect to see you here.' Ouch.

Richard Moran was a first-year teacher at Prahran High, who started at the same time as me. He would have been only in his mid-twenties; he was quite straight and proper but would readily break into a smile. He didn't put up with any crap, yet while he was strict you knew where you stood with him. He was the teacher that got me into reading—he did this purely by referring to books in class. I'm not sure if it was meant to trigger interest, but it did in me. Harper Lee's *To Kill a Mockingbird* and Hemingway's *The Old Man and the Sea* were two that he mentioned and they became favourites of mine.

Mr Moran would keep an eye out for me. I was class captain and we got along well from the start. One morning, during English class, he could see that I was not quite with it. He gave me a little bit of a hurry-up for being distracted. Then he got annoyed and asked me to stand up.

'Now, Mr Evans, can you tell me what I was talking to the class about, please?'

'No,' I answered.

'Then what is the problem this morning, Mr Evans? Please!'

He was building up a head full of steam but then backed off, which was a little out of character for him. A few minutes later he walked down to where I was sitting, while the class was working away. He leaned on my desk.

'What is going on with you today? What is the problem here?'

'It's my father's funeral today,' I said. 'I didn't want to go, so I came to school.'

Mr Moran's face went blank. He looked away for a moment, and then he put his hand on my shoulder.

'We haven't been told anything about this. I am so sorry.' By this time his face was as white as a sheet. He then asked a really stupid question: 'Are you sure?'

I didn't need to reply. He could see the answer for himself. No one had contacted the school to let them know Dad was gone. I'm certain my mother meant to but the call never was made.

Mr Moran said, almost to himself: 'I wonder what he died of?'

'Cancer,' I replied.

'No one here even knew he was sick. Why didn't you say something, Mark?'

I had no answer for him. Was it my job to say anything about it? I was confused; it was like I was outside of my body, watching the scene unfold. How *could* this happen? Why didn't he know and why did Dad have to die?

ϟ

In 1971, by the time I was fifteen, Dad now gone three years, my mum wanted to move out to a house at beachside

Seaford, about forty kilometres away, to be with her new partner, Jock Livingstone. I could understand why she wanted a new start with Jock, getting away from the Hilton and the memories of losing Dad. I had no issue with her leaving. I just wanted her to be happy again.

But I didn't want to change schools, so I stayed in our place at the Prahran Hilton and Mum agreed to check in with me regularly to ensure the joint was still standing. Mum certainly wasn't crazy about the arrangement at the outset but I had always been very independent; she had taught me how to look after myself domestically. Still, it definitely took some time for her to adjust. I was pretty lucky to have my own place at fifteen. Some place, though: the Hilton was infamous at the time as a launching pad for suicides. They'd ride the lift to the roof and jump.

I was once in the kitchen with a cute young lady by the name of Terri Mannix, who was a friend. As we talked, I saw something flash by the window, followed by this noise, which I could only describe as the sound of a hefty watermelon being hit by a truck. I had a bad feeling but went out to the balcony anyway. I had to have a look. I wish I hadn't: the image is burned into my subconscious. The jumper ended up looking like something by Picasso; it was horrible. It amazed me that a body could fall that far to the ground—twelve storeys—and not just blow apart. It was the first time I'd even seen a dead body. He'd landed on a logo that looked a bit like a spacecraft. I turned to Terri and said, 'At least he had something to aim for.' You could get a bit desensitised living at the Hilton.

My best friend was Graham Kennedy, who also lived at the Hilton. Graham was a Glaswegian; he'd once played soccer with my soon-to-be bandmate Malcolm Young, when he was about ten years old, on the streets of Cran Hill. Graham told me that his father Neil had seen a jumper at the Hilton on his way home from work. He described how this bloke fell straight down, with his arms by his side, feet first, 'like a bloody missile'. The poor guy planted himself in one of the project's freshly dug garden beds. One local wag described the jumper as 'our new garden gnome'. Someone approached me at a party with a Polaroid of the guy, asking me to sign and verify the thing, which was a bit much, even for me. (Polaroids were to become notorious on the road, particularly with a certain member of the AC/DC crew, who aptly renamed them 'Pornaroids'.)

When I was fifteen, a few of my mates and I were invited to a 'turn', as parties were called at the Hilton, that was being thrown by a bunch of older blokes. The proviso was that we brought along a dozen bottles of Vic Bitter and some girls. For some reason—still a complete mystery to me—girls were called 'brushes'. Anyway, we were walking along the first-floor balcony to the 'turn' when a partygoer came crashing through the flyscreen door, all the while getting a real thrashing from two huge guys.

After a very solid beating, one of the attackers said to the bloke: 'Come on, mate, up you get. Tidy yourself up now. You're all right, off you go, toddle off home.' Then he said to his partner, 'Give us a hand, will ya?' They picked up the poor punching bag and threw him straight off the balcony. When he landed, it sounded like a smaller watermelon this time. The big bloke looked at us, took the bottles and said: 'Thanks, boys. Where's the sheilas?'

Luckily, an assortment of bushes and shrubs broke some of the bloke's impact, but we thought he was another dead one, for sure. His attackers went inside but we didn't; we were still wondering what to do about the new addition to the garden. Maybe the party wasn't a good option after all.

Then I heard a voice from below.

'Hey—have they gone inside? Are they gone?'

It was the guy in the shrubs. I couldn't believe it. He was alive. We gave him the all-clear and up he got and took off like an Olympic sprinter, putting the big strides in, never to be seen again. I don't know what he had in his system—we had heard about 'speed' yet had no idea what it was; we were drinkers and nothing more—but this guy would have been sore as hell the next morning, or whenever the gear he was on backed off.

Still, my memories of the Hilton aren't all bad. I know I have mountains of reasons to hate the place, constantly being pushed around, threatened and beaten up. And the place was a shithouse, with a lot of deadbeats, deviants and weirdos hanging around all the time, plus the regular bashings and associated mayhem that went on. I lost my father while I was living there, too, so I really shouldn't have any affection for the joint. Yet I've always been of the opinion that memories are selective, if you have a positive outlook. It would have been easy for me to cry 'victim' and give up, or figure that the world owed me something because I'd had a rough start. But I've got no time for professional victims—some people endure unspeakable tragedy and still find a way to move on. Maybe my early training in shitty situations at the Hilton helped me later on in life, when I'd get seriously tested. You can learn a lot from watching people fuck up, if you have your head on straight. It's like a role model in reverse: I saw people fucking up and promised myself that

I'd never sink that low. Graham and I finally woke up when we started earning some money. I distinctly recall him saying, 'We have to get out of this shithole. Let's save up and go to London.' That was the plan. Even just having a plan, no, a *dream*, made me feel better. The idea of somehow getting away appealed to me.

Steve McGrath was another good mate of mine, a guy I met through football. He'd stay at the Hilton with me on weekends and we'd get up to things that teenage boys want to but usually couldn't—that is, inviting girls over to, erm, 'spend the night'. But this was Club 56, where pretty much anything went. Soon enough Steve would play his part in not just getting me out of the Hilton but introducing me to a whole new world of possibilities, going by the unlikely name of AC/DC.

Steve was a little put out when I found a steady girlfriend, Glynis Edwards. It put a rather large dent in our weekend shenanigans. Glynis was from Stevenage, England and was barely sixteen when she appeared, smiling, on the scene. She would stay over on weekends but virtually moved in when she found a job at a real estate agent in South Yarra. It does seem a little trailer trash-ish that a seventeen-year-old boy was living with a sixteen-year-old girl but our mothers were fine with the situation. And really, short of sending Glynis to a convent, it would have been going on regardless. We were real good mates, too, something that's been a trend for me in relationships with the ladies. I've always enjoyed female company. In the main I find them a lot more interesting than guys and not just for the physical reasons—but that can definitely get my attention, too. I've never been uncomfortable in the presence of women. I was shy, possibly, when I was young, but that's it.

There was always the opportunity to mix with girls in 'the flats'. There were at least a couple of thousand people living on the estate, so a good percentage had to be in my target demographic, i.e. female. I did like to share myself around before Glynis came on to the scene, and afterwards, too, with all due apologies to her.

I wasn't just mixing it with females of my age, either. Prior to hooking up with Glynis, I was given a very intense introductory course in sex education by a young, married mother of three who lived in our building. I got to know Helen (not her real name) just through saying hello, helping her out with the shopping, and basically being a good guy. You would have wanted to be a good guy around her, too. She was a hottie, in her late twenties when we first met. I was at her thirtieth birthday party, and Helen had a little too much to drink and made it very obvious to a lot of people that she had taken a shine to me. I was getting some pretty weird looks from some of the ladies, so I guessed they smelled a rat. Thankfully, hubby was pissed to the eyeballs and oblivious to the fact that his wife wanted to wear me as a hat.

I'm probably one of the few people on earth who lost his virginity when all he'd set out to do was wash his new pair of Lee Rider jeans, but that's how it happened. That is one of the great things about life—you just don't know what's around the corner. In my case it was Helen.

Each floor of the Hilton had its own common laundry, equipped with an industrial-size washer and an old-style freestanding spin dryer that used to make a hell of a racket and vibrate like crazy. I had just been to see Boris the Tailor, an old Jewish tailor who supplied us young guys with Levis and Lees, cowboy shirts and the like. I always got a discount because Boris was sweet on my mum. So, as we all know, you had to wash the stiffness out of new jeans or you'd be walking around like the Tin Man from *The Wizard of Oz*. Down to the laundry I went.

The spin dryer was gyrating away, as loud as ever, so Helen didn't hear me when I entered the laundry. At first I didn't get what she was up to, but I soon realised that the spin dryer was doing a job on the towels *and* Helen. I was stunned, frozen to the spot. 'What the fuck do I do here?' I wondered. I was close to taking off out the door at the speed of light when Helen looked over, and I can only assume she was too far gone to care. She reached over, got me in what I can best describe as a bear hug and dragged me to the floor. At that stage I was ready to shit blue lights.

Helen led the way, of course. I was fourteen and had no idea about sex. But that was how I lost my virginity, on a cold, hard concrete laundry floor. It was the start of a beautiful friendship.

As a kid growing up in the late 1960s and early 70s, I had two passions away from women: playing Australian Rules football with East Hawthorn Football Club, and music. I was a rover, an on-the-baller and a sneaky little fucker near the goals. Don't mind telling you, I loved kicking goals; all on-ballers do. One season I beat the future Melbourne and Victorian State of Origin captain, Robbie Flower, in a goal-kicking competition. I wanted to play football professionally and was mad keen about my team, Carlton. Still am. This was the era where Carlton reinvented the code and managed to keep robbing Collingwood in the big games, thanks to players like Alex Jesaulenko, John Nicholls, Sergio Silvagni, Robbie Walls and the guy who started it all, the great Ron Barassi.

I have a photo of me and Ron that takes pride of place in my bar. The photo was taken at a 'President's Lunch' before a game between the Sydney Swans and Melbourne at the SCG in 1997. It's surely one of the very few photos in which I'm wearing a tie, but you couldn't get in without one. Ron has always been a hero of mine, since he was Carlton's captain–coach in 1966. I've had the chance to chat with him a few times and it has always been a huge buzz. The guy is larger than life, bristles with character and is an absolute gentleman. He surely has the greatest smile in Australian sport. Some years later, I asked Ron to sign the photo at a Swans barbecue.

Ron looked at the photo, studied my face, looked me up and down and deadpanned: 'What happened?'

I got very serious about playing the game in my teens. I was sixteen when I played my first game for my new club, St Kilda City, feeder club for AFL (then VFL) team St Kilda. In the first minute a massive opponent and his well-directed elbow took me out. I went down in a heap and came to with one of the trainers telling me, 'That's about the worst broken nose I've ever seen, son.' Why, thank you so much. He was cleaning my face with a wet towel and said, 'How 'bout we fix it?'

He duly cupped his grimy hands either side of my nose and—Crack! Scrape! 'There you go,' he said. 'You'd never know.' At that point I was back on my feet but ready to pass out. I was spitting, swallowing and coughing up blood and seeing everything in black and white. My eyes were starting to close up. I made it to the quarter-time break and our coach came up and congratulated me for playing on.

'I thought he'd killed you,' he said, referring to my early knock. He asked me if I had another quarter in me. 'A little bit of pain won't hurt you.'

I did make it to half-time, and played okay, too, but during the break my eyes completely closed and that was it. I couldn't see for days afterwards. Football really was everything to me but self-preservation and the fact that I was zoned to play at St Kilda—in the unlikely event that I was good enough, big enough and actually survived—all went against my football future.

Music was sneaking up on the inside, anyway. I was immersed in music from day one. My father was a fan of the silky-smooth Nat King Cole. My mother preferred Frank Sinatra. But the fun really started with Laura and John. They had Elvis Presley, Eddie Cochran, Fats Domino, Jerry Lee Lewis, Little Richard and Buddy Holly blasting all the time. There was me, dancing my diapers off, smack dab in the middle of a house full of jivin' teenagers. The Beatles, the Stones and The Who would come into my life soon enough, courtesy of Judy. Years later, when I worked in the vintage guitar business, I got to know the Beatles' George Harrison, a real character and a gentleman.

When a few mates started messing around with guitars, well, that was it: count me in. I bought my first bass guitar for the reason that most players take the leap—out of necessity, because no one else wanted to play bass. I fancied myself another John Entwistle, The Who's killer bass player. I was never subjected to much in the way of formal music lessons, which may or may not come as a surprise to anyone who has heard me play. The few lessons I did have were courtesy of a great guitar player named Tony Naylor, who taught at Allan's Music on Collins Street in Melbourne. My pal Graham Kennedy and I took four lessons each and pretty much winged it from there.

The first real large-scale gig I ever saw, at Festival Hall in Melbourne with Graham, was a show by the English rock band Free. Although they shared the bill with Manfred Mann's Earth Band and Deep Purple, Free blew them both away. I was fifteen, and from that moment on I wanted to play in a band. They were just so cool and very young, too—their guitarist, Paul Kossoff, was only four years older than me. Suddenly, after seeing them, a life in rock and roll didn't seem so unrealistic to me: if these guys could get this far, well, why not? I'd seen other shows at Festival Hall, including Creedence Clearwater Revival, who were amazing, but Free were my pick.

The only time I disappointed my mother was when I knocked back her suggestion that I learn to play the bagpipes with the Caulfield City Pipe Band. I have no idea where that notion came from, but my mother could and still can be wonderfully eccentric at times. Imagine what the residents of the Hilton would have thought about me in a kilt! The irony, of course, is that some bagpipe expertise would have been more than handy when I joined AC/DC and we were recording 'It's a Long Way to the Top'. But how was I to know?

My mother did, however, encourage both Graham and me with our guitar playing. She always had an ear out listening to us slaughter the Rolling Stones, The Who and the rest of them, when she checked in with us at the Hilton. This was during our acoustic phase, but I can tell you it all wore a bit thin once electric guitars, amps and drums appeared on the scene. Loud apprentice rock bands are not welcomed with open arms in a twelve-storey concrete block of flats. My mother disapproved of the volume but always supported us; she saw music as a way of keeping us off the street and out of the police station. That had to be a good thing.

I bought my first bass from the Oriental Pearl Loan Office on Chapel Street, South Yarra, for twenty-two dollars. It was a pawnshop, a dank, dark, dusty cave of a place inhabited by a varied assortment of oddballs and misfits looking for a change of luck or for some mug to hustle. The shop did a roaring trade in 'second-hand goods'. It was run by a little guy named Neil who happily accepted an Education Department cheque that was actually intended for the purchase of textbooks for my fifth year at Prahran High School. That bass, a really bad copy of a Fender Precision bass, is the reason I play right-handed, even though I'm a natural leftie. I wanted to flip it over and play left-handed, like Paul McCartney, but the strings weren't long enough to reverse. The only fix would have been to buy a new set of bass strings, but I didn't have another Education Department cheque handy. So I taught myself to play right-handed.

Being a leftie definitely had its drawbacks. My first-grade teacher—an absolute horror of a woman—couldn't abide left-handers and would seat all the 'afflicted' students on the left-hand side of the desks. She would patrol the aisles with a wooden ruler and whack you on the knuckles if she caught you with a pencil in your left hand. So we lefties were beaten into being right-handed. She also used to belt anyone unfortunate enough to stammer, the sour old bitch.

I didn't expend much time or energy at Prahran High; most of my education has been self-inflicted. In the five and a bit years that I was there I don't think I ever attended a week in full. I was always skipping days. And I didn't do a jot of homework either—and I mean not ever. Yet I managed to blag my way through, and decided to apply for a studentship, a scholarship that was intended to pay my way through teachers' college. Teaching would also qualify me for ten weeks' annual leave, and that certainly had its appeal. The odd thing about my time at Prahran High was that I failed only one subject, and miserably, too. That subject? Music, of course.

School was almost a part-time thing for me. Technically I wasn't skipping school because my mother knew all about it. It wasn't her style to force me to attend, but I can't recall her even talking to me about it. I suppose if my grades suffered badly it might have been different.

It's no coincidence that the subjects I did enjoy were invariably taught by teachers I liked. English was my favourite; as long as I can remember I've been fascinated by words and how they work. By the time I got to Prahran High I had started to read seriously, but for some reason the books that were set on the course went mostly unread, such as J.D. Salinger's *The Catcher in the Rye*. Do people write books like that purely to drive schoolkids nuts?

History and geography were also fine by me. I was learning about other countries, something that was always going to hold my attention, likewise Miss Starr, the history teacher. She was tiny, not classically beautiful, but put together like no one else I'd ever met. It was as if God was seeing how much He could get away with. Maths absolutely baffled me; it was like another language, which I guess it is in a lot of ways.

Algebra remains a mystery to me, although my youngest daughter Virginia is nursing me through year-eight maths. The sciences were a pain in my butt; the only part that got me going was astronomy. Now that was cool—still is.

Football was a large part of school, too, even if the inter-school games against Richmond and Fitzroy High were more like unarmed combat. I'm glad I played for Prahran High, because we had some real psychopaths on our team. One guy would play the whole game pretending to be a cowboy, running along, slapping his butt, making out that he was riding a horse, all the while bellowing ear-shattering 'yee-hahs'. During one game he smacked an opponent and knocked him clean out. When the umpire sent him off he explained, 'But he was dancing with the sheriff's girl.' Another one of our guys was apt to ride an imaginary motorcycle. We never lost a game.

Chapter 2

'You're barred, you little prick.'

There was an old, unused cinema on Chapel Street, down past the pawnshop where I bought my first bass, that hosted a regular music gig called That's Life. It was directly opposite Windsor station and had been refitted in a piss-poor effort to make it appear like a cool nightclub. It was famous for the hand-to-hand combat that went on there between the Sharpies and the Mods. It was one of the many halls and theatres that featured bands on Friday and Saturday nights. These were non-licensed venues so no alcohol was served; consequently there was no age restriction like a pub, although industrial amounts of beer were consumed on the way to the gig. And a hip flask of Scotch was viewed as the cool thing to have on board, along with a taped-up roll of two-cent coins, which fitted perfectly into a clenched fist, if and when required. All this action was within walking distance of my place at the Prahran Hilton.

We—that is, me and my band buddies, Graham, Micky

and Norm—would head off to Life, as it was known, or to venues like Garrison on High Street, Ormond Hall, Opus at St Kilda City Hall or the Try Boys Club on Surrey Road. We got to see the best recording acts of the day, including the Master's Apprentices, Billy Thorpe and the Aztecs, Doug Parkinson in Focus, Chain, and Carson, featuring the magnificent Broderick Smith out front on vocals. He'd later front one of my all-time faves, the Dingoes.

It was always a bit dicey at Try Boys, as the Surrey Road Gang resided there. These were serious people; the rumour going around was that one of their crew had been killed in a street fight and his cohorts had opted for a home cremation, scattering his ashes in the Prahran pool late at night. This story stuck around over the years, and because of the reputation of some of the individuals alleged to be involved, I had no reason to doubt it. One school buddy of mine, Wade Dix, was close to this crew, as was his brother Lee. Their dad was in the Painters and Dockers Union, who ran the Port Melbourne wharves at the time. Quite a few items turned up in the pubs in Prahran that 'fell off the back of a boat' and I have no doubt that Dix Senior was involved in it up to his bloodshot eyeballs.

Wade became very close to my mother over the years; I'm sure she would have adopted him if he was up for grabs. Wade was an olive-skinned kid and a little guy, too, like me. He was having a rough time, which a continuing series of lumps, bumps, cuts and bruises seemed to confirm. He had a stack of reasons not to be the happy soul that he was, but his upbeat nature was something that endeared him to my mother. She went from 'Mrs E' to Mum in record time for Wade. Wade later found a novel way to get a few weeks off work; he'd put one of his fingers in a sheet metal press. Off came the top half of the digit and away he went on four weeks compo. Wade's brother worked out that he could get another nine months off work at that rate, digit by bloody digit.

On New Year's Day 1969 my mates and I all went to That's Life for a special afternoon show sponsored by radio station 3XY, the local top-forty station. Their playlist featured the Beatles, the Stones, the Kinks, the Beach Boys, the Monkees, the Easybeats—all the hit makers of the time, along with the one-hit wonders, the near-myths and unfortunately large slabs of 'bubblegum' music, an offensive brand of sickly-sweet pop music, as peddled by such 'bands' as the Archies and the 1910 Fruitgum Company.

Featured on the New Year's bill was a band called Compulsion. They had a Maori guy named Reno on guitar, who was a Jimi Hendrix clone. They were managed by a fellow named Michael Browning, who owned Sebastians and Berties, two major Melbourne rock venues. The other band on the bill was the Valentines, from Perth. They had half a hit at the time with 'My Old Man's a Groovy Old Man', which was written by George Young and Harry Vanda, the songwriting team for sixties legends the Easybeats and solid-gold Oz rock royalty, even if they were Scottish and Dutch, in that order.

The Valentines were a teenybopper band, a prototype for later groups like the Bay City Rollers. They wore uniforms of tight-fitting flares, high-heeled boots and hippie-looking shirts with see-through chiffon sleeves—all in orange. They were a good band, and featured two lead singers, but they were a bit too poppy for me. (Compulsion's Jimi Hendrix covers were more to my taste.) And it was very hard to get past those unearthly orange outfits. They were a huge hit with the girls, though, and had their own fan club, who screamed their lungs out and carried signs that read: BE MY VALENTINE IN '69.

The Valentines kicked off their set with a bunch of Motown tunes and they were lively, I'll give them that. The main singer was a guy named Vince Lovegrove, but it was the other vocalist that caught my eye. He obviously had a few under his belt but had space for a few more. I was sitting in front of the PA on the side of the stage and I could see him disappear into the wings during solos and after songs to slug from a bottle of Johnnie Walker. Then he'd walk back on stage and roar into the microphone. He had a bit of style about him even in the ghastly orange get-up. As the set progressed he built up a decent sweat and I could see something strange going on under the sheer chiffon sleeves. Tattoos were starting to appear—he had tried to hide them with make-up but the sweat was making it run. This guy was turning into Bon Scott before my eyes.

That was the first time I saw Bon. I thought he was dead cool, even though he was tiny compared to the others in the band. Bon stood about five foot five, tops, but he had a real look of mischief about him. The tattoos and the rapidly emptying bottle of Scotch were very impressive to this schoolkid, let me tell you. But things didn't work out so well for Reno from Compulsion, the band that opened for the Valentines. He was a knockout on guitar but he got a bit carried away on drugs and started robbing banks. He got pinched when he went into a bank to do a job and was so out of it that he didn't realise it was his own branch. Go directly to jail, do not pass go, do not collect $200—and that was the end of Compulsion.

I subsequently followed Bon Scott's career via the music paper *Go Set*, as he moved on to his next band, Fraternity, who were a full-on hippie band, living out the Woodstock dream on a property at Aldgate in the Adelaide Hills. They wanted to be the Australian answer to The Band, Bob Dylan's legendary backing outfit that became one of the most influential and respected groups of the late sixties and early seventies. However, Bon's verdict on Fraternity was this: 'We all got stoned and disappeared up our own arseholes.' The next time I saw Bon was at my local, the Station Hotel in Prahran, six years later.

ϟ

Along with Graham Kennedy and some schoolmates from Prahran High School who had similar taste in music, we formed a band basically from scratch. We put in some serious practice and before too long we were playing a bunch of Free tunes like 'All Right Now', 'Ride on a Pony' and 'Fire and Water', along with the occasional Deep Purple rocker like 'Speed King' and a liberal lashing of Status Quo. As with all young bands, there were lengthy discussions, sometimes heated, as to what to call this new group that was surely destined for superstardom. Graham, who was a Mickey Mouse fan, suggested Steamboat Willy, after the name of the very first Mickey Mouse cartoon. Eventually we went with Judd, which was the surname of our drummer, Lincoln Judd.

The band consisted of Graham on guitar and vocals, Lincoln on drums and me on bass. We were all dead keen on getting the band going—gigging was all we wanted to do. That, we deemed, was the 'big time'. We did our first gig at the 1973 New Year's Eve party hosted by Graham's sister, Maureen. By a strange coincidence, AC/DC was playing their first show that night too, some 800 kilometres north at the Chequers nightclub in Sydney.

That very first Judd gig was at Maureen's home in Montmorency. Maureen and her husband Harold always put on a great New Year's Eve party—still do. It was a family-and-friends affair; there were maybe sixty or seventy people there, with a few of our mates as well. I had the jitters before we started. I thought I was nervous but came to realise it was anticipation, nervous energy.

We set up in their quite large lounge room, sneaked a few drinks and off we went. I think our volume was a bit of a shock to the partygoers but we were a rock band and the last thing we wanted to do at our first gig was to compromise. As soon as we started playing, whoosh, all my pre-gig nerves disappeared. It felt great.

Once we got a little chemistry going, played a few gigs and started to get some reaction, we thought, 'Hey, we can do this.' Then we agreed that we needed some original songs, and this, while admirable and principled, did lead to some woeful attempts at songwriting, god-awful rip-offs of the cover tunes we already had in our set.

Still, Judd did some gigs, played a few more parties, and we pulled a girl or two, but Graham was the first of us to grab a real opportunity. The best-known band in Prahran was called Fat Bubbles—I kid you not—and was run by the Madaferri brothers, Peter and Mark. Graham soon joined them. He was out gigging two to three times a week, while I was looking for another band, waiting for my own opportunity.

My school days came to an abrupt end early in my sixth year at Prahran High. It had become obvious that I was wasting both my time and my teachers' on the rare occasions that I turned up at school. It was during the break between terms that I sat the public service entrance exam. My sister had a well-paid government job in what the locals called the 'big green toilet block' at the eastern end of Spring Street in the city. The BGTB housed many government departments; the place was home to thousands of pen-pushers.

While I was waiting to sit the exam I applied for three other jobs, did the interviews and got offered the lot. This must seem galling to today's school leavers but we are talking about different times. Jobs were relatively easy to come by if you weren't too fussy; it was possible to leave school without too much thought about what the future might hold. In my case, there was no thought involved, and absolutely no consultation with my mother. I think she was impressed that I showed the initiative to get out and sit the public service exam. Then again, she didn't know that I was doomed to certain failure at Prahran High and had to jump ship.

I was told I was the youngest of the hundred-plus people that sat the exam on that day. It wasn't a particularly long exam, maybe an hour, but there was plenty packed in there. Instructions were along the lines that there was a lot to answer, so get on with it, as not a lot of applicants complete the paper. So I ripped into it. There was smoke coming off my pencil, I swear. There were questions like: 'What is an ICBM?' (We were given four choices, but for the record it's an Intercontinental Ballistic Missile.) 'In what country does the Pope reside?' It was all geared to get you unbalanced, I believe. I got it done, gave it the once-over, then looked around and noticed everyone else still hard at work. After a few minutes an elderly supervisor came over and asked if everything was okay.

'Yes,' I said, 'but I'm not sure I was given the entire exam.'

The supervisor flicked through the pages. 'That's it. You've answered it all, you can go. Excellent work, young man.'

At that precise moment I learned what pure hatred looks like: it was directed at me from everyone else in the exam room. The fact that I had answered everything could have pissed off the troops, but what inspired near mutiny was the fact that it'd taken me a shade under twenty minutes.

While I waited on news from the public service, I took a job with GTE Sylvania as a trainee storeman. GTE Sylvania was a US lighting company famous for inventing the flash-cube used in cameras. I spent forever packing boxes of the fucking things in a massive warehouse with a concrete floor during a Melbourne winter. It was freezing. It's a miracle that I was able to father any children; it was like having an epidural, or at least that's what I imagine an epidural would feel like.

More time passed and there was no word from the public service. Then one evening there was a knock on my door. An old chap with a handful of letters stood there. 'These may be for you—are you Mark W. Evans?' The mail had been going to 56 Surrey Road instead of 56/1 Surrey Road. No excuses now: the public service beckoned.

And so began a pretty mundane existence. I was doing fine financially—if that was even important then—holding down what my grandfather, Will, proclaimed to be 'a job for life' in the public service. I was a Class 1 Clerk in the pay section of the Postmaster-General's Department. My new pal and mentor was a bloke named Peter Stevenson. 'Stevo' showed me the gig and was the guy who knew where all the bodies were buried in our building at 172 William Street, on the west side of the city. It was a miracle I lasted as long as I did in the PMG pay section, but that was a lot to do with having Stevo around. He was in his mid-twenties and 'adopted' me; he was just one of those guys you wanted to be around, a real character. Stevo was an ex-Prahran guy who'd realised it was a good idea to get out of there as quickly as possible.

I started on about $140 a fortnight, which was plenty of dough for a young guy. I spent loads on clothes and bought a new record player. I also bought a lounge suite for my mum, had our flat carpeted and generally chipped in financially for the first time in my life.

The work was pretty ordinary, but there were good times and laughs to be had at lunchtime, when I'd hit the pub for a counter lunch—or two, I needed to gain weight for football, which I was still playing—washing down the bangers and mash, shepherd's pie or porterhouse steak with a few beers. The pub beckoned again after work, with the lure of more icy-cold beer and the pool table. I had taken to playing pool very quickly when I started work at sixteen; the lifers at the after-work pubs in the city took me a little too lightly on the felt, especially with all that beer on board. I managed to pick up a few extra dollars.

It was at this point in my life that music really started to take over from football as a possible career—all the late nights, drinking and carousing at Club 56 was taking the edge off my fitness. There was just too much fun going on and music was a big part of that. I was going out to gigs at pubs ('Fancy a beer, mate?') or sitting around with the guys plucking away on the acoustics ('Feel like another beer?') or playing gigs and parties ('Better get some more beer, just in case'). And when I was going to the footy, well, it was just un-Australian not to have a beer. Or a few.

I kicked off 1975 with a brand-new bass rig, a 300-watt all-tube beast with two cabinets loaded with arse-kicking JBL speakers. The rig had come courtesy of my job and some one-off gigs. Frankly, that was the best thing to come out of my stint with the public service: a decent bass set-up—and a few good friendships, of course.

My job was mind- and arse-numbing. I had been there almost two years and was still on probation. Generally after six months you were 'confirmed' and hired on a permanent basis. In my case this didn't happen because of my attendance record and 'a problem with authority'. At least that's what the counsellor called it.

Stevo looked after me, though, showed me the ropes and, crucially, authorised the overtime. Hello, bass rig, and hello to the front bars of the many pubs on the west side of the city: the Golden Age, Great Western, Mitre Tavern. It was a very straight world compared to one I'd soon encounter, but fun nonetheless. There was plenty of Carlton Draught at lunch plus introductions to a few ladies in the typing pool and personnel. I spent much of Saturday afternoon overtime on the floor of the typing pool with a very attractive—but very married—young lady, or playing cards with the guys. I preferred the floor of the typing pool; even without my well-stacked married friend it was a good place for a nap after lunch. But those nylon carpet tiles can really do your knees in. I suffered some nasty carpet burns.

I went on four weeks' leave in mid-January 1975. I was flush with holiday pay—over $500, a massive amount to me—and hit the Grosvenor Hotel with the guys for a send-off. After a couple of beers I was straight to the pool table, with the line from Rod Stewart's 'Maggie May' about making 'a living out of playing pool' swimming in my head. And I couldn't miss—everything I looked at went in, much to the chagrin of the older patrons who were trying to relieve 'the young bloke' of his holiday dollars.

The usual gambit when a player was 'on' was, of course, to get him pissed, and wear him down to a point where he'd be making stupid bets and all of a sudden the mug was trying to win his own money back. That was the plan for my $500 and me. If someone had a pocket of cash in a city pub on a Friday night, well, word got around the pub fast and the plotting would start. *Et tu, pisspot.* What the vultures didn't know was that I had some solid local knowledge and advice from my older workmates, especially Stevo, who was there with me. The side betting had now begun and we were well ahead. It became apparent that we were in for a long night; there was no way we could make a painless exit when we were that far in front.

Stevo helped me through, sorting out the beers—with an added shot of vodka—that were bought for me. He handed me some No-Doz, saying, 'Take these, they'll keep the piss off you.' He was spot on. The pills seemed to counteract any stray vodka that got into my system, even though I was wired.

My eventual exit was Stevo's idea. He suggested I make a big deal of putting twenty dollars on the bar—a lot of beers in 1975—buying a round for all, leaving the cash on the bar and announcing loudly: 'I gotta take a piss!'

Stevo whispered in my ear: 'Now, go into the pisser and keep going, head straight through into the Saloon Bar, out onto Little Collins Street and FUCK OFF very quickly. I'll clean up when they suss that you've bolted.'

Stevo waited for one beer, and then shouted to a mate, 'What do you mean he's fucked off? He's got all my fucking money!' and charged into Little Collins Street in the opposite direction to me, followed by half the pub.

I ended up at home before midnight, wide-eyed and still wired, with more than $1000 in my pocket. That amount of money was simply unbelievable, but not as hard to believe as getting out of the pub without a hiding. I don't know if it was the cash or the No-Doz, but I didn't sleep until Sunday night.

I spoke to Stevo a few days later. I was primed for some kind words and maybe even thanks for the big Friday win.

'Just a little friendly advice, Mark,' he said. 'Never, ever go back to the Grosvenor Hotel.'

The office was only a ten-minute tram ride away from Prahran, but after I came back from leave I struggled to get to work on time, if I made it there at all. After my probation period had been extended for the fourth time—a record, perhaps?—I was called into the office of one Mr Nicholls. He was a public servant of nearly twenty years' grind, a Class 8 Clerk, high up the food chain and very obviously a lifer. I really did like the guy, but he was painfully straight, and had the look of a bloke whose shoes were a few sizes too small. We were on completely different wavelengths; he was basically treading water until he retired, which to me seemed like a living hell.

So the meeting began with Mr Nicholls droning on about how obviously intelligent I was, telling me that I was wasting the opportunity of a lifetime by not applying myself.

'You'd be wise to consider your future in the service,' he told me, absolutely straight-faced. 'And do something about your hair. You can't be taken seriously with hair like that.' I'd adopted a 'just let it grow' hairstyle, which, in truth, was probably more suited to a rock and roll band than the public service.

He thought he was doing the right thing; he just didn't know any other way and was completely blinkered to life's possibilities. He only wanted to help out a 'young fellow with a rosy future'. He was being polite and considerate, I'm certain his heart was in the right place, but all this was lost on me because I started to nod off. Bosses don't like their staff falling asleep when they are handing out pearls of wisdom and he decided to give it to me.

'HOW CAN YOU EXPECT TO BE WHERE I AM IN FIFTEEN YEARS IF YOU DON'T PULL YOUR SOCKS UP?'

'Fuck me,' I thought to myself. 'Be here in fifteen years? In your chair?'

The lecture ended when I replied, 'You can stick that up your arse,' and walked out. That was it. I returned later on to pick up my last pay but because of all my time off it amounted to $7.54, from memory. The personnel officer insisted that I shouldn't resign but instead take a twelve-month leave of absence, without pay.

'You'll be back,' she said.

I think she was a little disappointed to see me go as we had built up a relationship, mainly in the back seat of her car after work. My pals couldn't believe I was schtupping a lady in her early thirties and I was interrogated at length about our backseat shenanigans. Thankfully I was discreet enough not to compromise my relationship with the lady. I'd like to think I was being a gentleman, but in my heart I know it's much more likely that I was a greedy little pig.

One of the more senior women in personnel had taken a shine to me (a purely platonic one, I must add) and told me that she didn't want me to 'throw away my career'. She really was a sweetheart and I feel a bit shabby that I can't recall her full name, but Margaret, if you happen to read this, all is well and I thank you for your concern. You were a real darling to care and I can still hear your friendly advice whenever I cast my mind back to my pre-AC/DC life.

'Mark,' she said, with absolute sincerity, 'music is not a career like the public service.'

Margaret, you have no idea how right you were.

In March 1975, not long after my nineteenth birthday, I was drinking icy-cold beer and playing pool—are you seeing a pattern here?—at the Station Hotel in Prahran with my old mate, Steve McGrath. Steve had been spending a lot of time at my place at the Prahran Hilton. His family lived in an outer suburb, Springvale, and although he didn't speak about it much his home life didn't seem to be overly happy. What I did know was that he was having some serious strife with his dad, who owned a chain of army disposal stores and was on Steve's back to go into the family business. So he pretty much moved in with me. We were both teenagers but we had some very interesting times at Club 56 with the local young ladies.

A special place of interest for us was the nurses' quarters at the Alfred Hospital, just down Commercial Road, next door to the Chevron Hotel. The trainee nurses (or at least some of them) took a real shine to Steve and myself and adopted a 'hands-on' attitude to our education. For that I'll be forever thankful.

Anyway, as we sipped our beers at the Station, Steve and I got to talking.

'What have you been doing for work, mate?' I asked him. It was a purely innocent question, but one that would change my life.

'I'm working with this new band called AC/DC. In fact, they need a bass player—what are *you* doing right now?' was Steve's answer.

Things had been a little quiet on the band front for me. I was playing with a bunch of older guys and, while I was learning from them, I knew that it wasn't what I wanted to do forever. The saving grace was that the guitar player was a fan of Irish guitarist Rory Gallagher and was dead keen on playing some high-octane blues. Eugene, the drummer, was also cool, although the keyboard player was inflexible—he wanted to do only Elton John tunes, ideally the entire *Goodbye Yellow Brick Road* album. (Keyboard players tend to give me the creeps, unless their names happen to be Fats Domino, Little Richard or Jerry Lee Lewis.) I still feel queasy just thinking about it. I always seemed to be the youngest in any band I played in.

My immediate future with music was bleak. My monster bass rig was sharing my bedroom with me (and Glynis). The silver domes in the centre of each of the JBL K140s were clearly visible when I was in bed; they seemed to be looking at me, mocking me. 'Are we going to be doing something soon, or are we all going to just sit here doing fuck-all?' It was such a cool rig but there I was, lying in bed, thinking something good had to happen soon or I would go completely nuts. It was bad enough already that my bass rig was talking to me.

I knew what I wanted. I wanted to be the bass player in a loud, nasty rock and roll band along the lines of Billy Thorpe and the Aztecs or the Coloured Balls. My guiding lights were ZZ Top and blues guys like Rory Gallagher, Johnny Winter and Freddie King. I was discovering the blues legends that inspired the Rolling Stones: Robert Johnson, Muddy Waters, Buddy Guy, Willie Dixon and Howlin' Wolf, who, in my eyes, was the greatest of them all.

What I was hearing in their recordings, some of which dated back to the 1930s, was an earthiness. The sound was bare and acoustic and these guys were wailin'. Their emotion, passion, anger and danger oozed out of the speakers. These guys were real, singing and playing and bleeding from genuine experience.

So there was my bass rig, in my bedroom, calling my name. I knew the kind of band I wanted to play in would definitely not involve Elton John tunes. It had to be loud, with two guitars like the Stones, nasty and blues-based. Where could I find a band like that? And would they need a bass player?

That one question from Steve was enough to change absolutely everything for me. I have often wondered what would have happened if I didn't ask him what he was up to. Still playing pool and getting pissed after work on a Friday night? The coast may be clear at the Grosvenor Hotel by now.

Although not musically inclined, Steve had scored some work with AC/DC as a roadie. I had heard of the band—I'd also heard something about one of them dressing as a schoolboy, complete with a satchel on his back.

Steve filled me in. 'They're a hard rock band,' he said. 'They just released an album—and they play a lot of Stones covers. It's right up your alley.'

Interesting, I thought.

He also mentioned that two of the guys in the band were George Young's little brothers. Now that really got my attention. As a kid, as soon as I saw the Easybeats on TV, I became a huge fan. George and his former Easybeats partner, Harry Vanda, had recently produced a super album by Stevie Wright, who was the Easybeats singer, called *Hard Road.* It included a tune called 'Evie: Parts I, II and III' that was a monster hit, even though it ran for over seven minutes. That was really something out of the ordinary—singles just didn't last more than three minutes. It was the start of a golden run for George and Harry. My only other knowledge of AC/DC at the time was the posters on the wall at the Hard Rock Café proclaiming AC/DC ARE CUM'N.

Steve gave me an address on Lansdowne Road in East St Kilda, a neighbouring suburb, which was the band's HQ. It was directly across Dandenong Road from the apartment of my sister Judy. Late on a Saturday afternoon in March 1975 I made my way over there. A very attractive young lady answered the door. She invited me in and explained that she was Angus Young's girlfriend. I have to tell you I was impressed; she was something else, cute as a button. She told me the guys were playing an afternoon gig at the Matthew Flinders Hotel in nearby Chadstone. 'They'll be back soon,' she told me. 'Want to wait?' That was an offer I could not refuse.

Chateau AC/DC was a large, unkempt single-storey house that would now be worth a stack. Back then, however, East St Kilda was more than a tad gamey, with many a massage parlour and a transient junkie population. All of the band and their crew, which consisted of Ralph the Roadie and Tana Douglas, lived at the house. Tana, their stagehand, must have been the first female roadie in Australia, and she did a fine job, too.

I had a look around. There was a sunroom at the front that led into the main hallway. Off the hallway were a number of bedrooms and a lounge room, with a family room sort of arrangement out the back. At this stage, I had no idea that Bon Scott was in the band, but I soon found out that the family room was his private domain.

Most of the guys returned a short while later—and as soon as I saw them I knew I wanted the gig. The reason? I recognised Phil Rudd. Phil was held in very high esteem among we gig-goers and wannabe musos. He'd played drums in a band called Buster Brown that had been a staple around the local pubs. I was surprised to see Phil—I didn't know if he had split from Buster Brown or if the band had gone arse up. Either way, I was real keen to get involved.

A couple of things about AC/DC struck me straight away. One was their stature, or lack thereof. Now, I'm not a tall guy, I'm only five-six on a good day, but these guys made me feel tall, particularly Malcolm and Angus. I couldn't recall meeting anyone smaller than Angus, and on seeing him the whole school uniform thing fell into place. It was perfect. The other thing that struck me was their attitude. They didn't know me from a bar of soap—and going by their scruffy appearance, that may well have been in short supply—so I didn't expect a group hug, but there was a coldness about them that I hadn't experienced before. It did have me wondering about them; matter of fact, still does!

We started talking about the gig. While in Melbourne, Malcolm's brother George had been filling in as their bassist, but George had to return to his family in Sydney and his commitment to Albert Productions—AC/DC's record company—where he was the house producer, so they were now working as a four-piece, with Malcolm on bass. We spoke at length about the band; I gave them an insight into what I was into and things rolled from there. I said one thing to Malcolm that I think stuck in his head. When we were talking about favourite players, I mentioned that my go-to guy was Gerry McAvoy, who played with Rory Gallagher.

'I want to be able to nail it like he does,' I said to Malcolm. 'No bullshit, nothing fancy, just rock-solid bass playing.' Malcolm didn't say anything; he just took it in.

It must have gone well because I left the house with a copy of their album *High Voltage*, with directions to learn the songs for a 'blow'—a jam session—with the guys the following afternoon. I was also told that if it came together I would be on the same money as the other guys, sixty dollars cash a week, about half what I had been earning in the public service, with accommodation thrown in at Lansdowne Road. Thankfully that was not necessary; it was a tad crowded already.

That money would be paid by their managers, Michael Browning and Bill Joseph, as part of a recent deal they had struck. I found out it was basically a rescue package. The band had been left stranded by their previous manager in Adelaide, and Michael and Bill repatriated the guys to Melbourne and saved their bacon. The guys referred to Michael simply as 'Browning' and seemed to regard him with some suspicion. A possible source of that might have been the managerial mess brother George ended up in with the Easybeats. I overheard conversations regarding 'legal action in England'.

So I was off home to spend a Saturday night learning their album and preparing for the audition. I liked the album, but couldn't connect the impression I had of the guys, and their taste in music, with tunes on the record like 'Love Song'. On the one hand, you had this group of young toughs—I hadn't met Bon as yet—who were into playing hard rock and were obviously living the rock and roll lifestyle. Then there was this schmaltzy piece of I-don't-know-what called 'Love Song'—it was in direct contrast to the rest of the album, which included the great blues tune 'Baby Please Don't Go' and Chuck Berry's 'School Days'. The other originals on the record were also a bit poppy. What little I knew of Malcolm, Phil and Angus didn't mesh with what I was hearing. I just couldn't see the marauding hordes of Sharpies at the suburban beer barns putting up with 'Love Song'. It seemed like a perfect way to cop a hiding, to be honest. All these questions and more would be cleared up rather smartly.

I arrived at the house at the agreed time on Sunday, with my gear, and took a look around at the guys. They must have done at least one show the night before and they looked a bit the worse for wear. Angus, especially, seemed to have been dragged through a hedge backwards. He was an absolute mess. I asked him if he had hit it very hard the night before. Was he hungover?

'I don't drink, mate,' he told me.

I thought it was a joke. I couldn't figure how he could look that ironed out without hitting the booze. As I'd learn that afternoon, he seemed to survive on cigarettes and tea. He had a killer of a cough, too. Angus reminded me of a little old man, which was pretty alarming at the time because he was only nineteen. That impression, of course, changed when he started playing.

After some small talk, more coughing from Angus and another cup of tea, the gear was set up in the hallway and away we went. I had a fair idea what to expect from Phil but I was completely unprepared for the Malcolm-and-Angus show. I wasn't that experienced but I knew this was something else. Their guitars drilled into you. It wasn't just the volume, although a couple of Marshall Super Lead 100-watt heads going hard in a hallway can kick up a fair bit of dust. No, it was their intensity and all-out attack that got me. We were playing the songs from the album but they were way more aggressive than the recording. I found out that Phil had joined after the album was cut and had only been with them a few weeks. That explained some of the extra wallop.

We ran through most of the tunes from *High Voltage*, although I did notice that 'Love Song' was omitted. My guess was that it was on its way out even then. Things went well; my impression was that Mal particularly enjoyed being back on guitar. What was immediately apparent to me was how well the guitars worked together, and, of course, the sheer volume they generated. I was glad I had the foresight to go for a big 300-watt bass amp, because I needed it to keep up with Mal and Angus.

Mal was the guy in the driver's seat. He set up the tunes with the tempos and grooves, and we were ripping along.

Even though it was my introduction to the guys on a playing level it sounded very, very good to me. I got a few directions along the way from Mal, who said things like, 'The last guy couldn't get this one together, that's why you're here.' (The identity of this 'last guy' was never revealed.) It wasn't all that comforting, but as I was to come to realise, AC/DC had fuck-all to do with feeling comfortable on a personal level, or any level, in fact. Still, there was plenty of volume, plenty of punch and smiles all round. 'This is going to work,' I thought to myself. 'I want this gig. This is the gig I've been searching for.'

We took a tea-and-ciggie break and there was some small talk regarding what I was doing work-wise. I knew that my job at the public service wouldn't survive; nothing was mentioned about me formally quitting, it was just taken for granted. This was my first indicator as to how AC/DC functioned: you weren't asked if anything was suitable, you did what the band demanded, pure and simple. There was no introductory course. If you were in, you were in for the benefit of the band and that went without saying. It was implicit.

During my audition I learned that Bon Scott was in the band, although he wasn't around on the day. All I was told was, 'Bon's not here,' nothing more. But that was another plus—Phil Rudd, the Youngs and Bon Scott all in the one group!

The informal audition seemed to go well. We all seemed to be on the same wavelength but it was odd being the tallest person in the band. While the guys were definitely on the cool side of friendly, what I did note was their solidarity. They were very obviously a band, living together, doing the hard yards and presenting a united front. This wasn't manufactured; it was natural, unaffected and I wanted in, badly. These guys meant business. In all, we played for an hour or so and hung out—punctuated by more coughing from Angus—and I was invited to watch the band play on the following Tuesday night. Of all places, the gig was at the Station Hotel in Prahran, my local. Mal would be playing bass so I offered him the use of my gear.

Ralph offered me a lift home to Prahran in Swivel Hips, the group's truck, which was so named because it would never keep in a straight line. It was only a ten-minute walk, but he was insistent. En route, we had a chat. He said he thought I had the gig and he proceeded to give me the lowdown on the set-up. A couple of things that Ralph told me really stuck in my mind.

Ralph had worked with Bon in Fraternity, both in Oz and in England, driving the bus. Ralph told me that they used to call Bon 'Ronnie Roadtest', because he would try anything, anytime. For a young guy like me, this was all pretty exciting.

'Let me give you a friendly piece of advice,' Ralph continued. 'It's Malcolm's band and it would be an excellent idea to remember that.'

'Gee, thanks, Ralph,' I thought, but kept it to myself.

Ralph dropped me off at the Hilton and said: 'Good on ya, mate, look forward to working with you. Oh, and the plan is that we'll be in England in a year.'

As I walked inside, I honestly didn't think there was a snowball's chance in hell of the band being in the UK within a year—and I was dead right. It would take a year and ten days.

I felt that the blow went okay and we seemed to get along well enough, even if they were a bit icy. But I was feeling a little anxious. I wanted in, but was uncertain—I basically didn't know the guys at all. It was risky but exciting at the same time and, realistically, I was fooling myself to think a better situation lurked just around the corner. As Phil would soon tell me, after I left they had a chat regarding my suitability. Malcolm, as usual, would have the first and last word.

'If he plays as good as he talks, he's in.'

I may not have been overly chatty, but I think my 'no-bullshit bass playing' line must have struck a chord with Malcolm Young.

There was one little problem. I had been at the Station Hotel the Saturday night before our jam and a cracker of a bar-room brawl erupted, which was par for the course in an inner-suburban pub. There wasn't enough room for a cat this night, let alone swinging one in the old front bar, so a few of us looking on got sucked into the melee.

I got hit by a flying jug of beer. It got me right across the front of the face and knocked the crap out of me. When I came to I was outside on the sidewalk in Greville Street—evidently I'd been thrown out for starting the trouble. I was busy spitting blood and checking it for teeth when Albert and Marino, the owners, came outside and told me I was barred from the pub. I thought, 'Fancy getting thrown out for getting smacked in the teeth with a jug of beer!'

For those who have never been hit by a full jug of beer, let me tell you it hurts like hell when you finally regain consciousness. It's not a sharp pain but a real heavy dull ache, as if someone had dropped something very heavy on your face from a great height. I do not recommend it under any circumstances. It was just like in the cartoons, when some poor sap gets an anvil dropped on their noggin. I had got away with a fair bit of crap in the Station in the years before that so when they barred me, I thought, 'Fuck it, who needs this place?' I certainly didn't, at least not until the next Tuesday.

So now I'm off to the Station Hotel on 19 March 1975 to check out AC/DC. I was feeling good, looking forward to a few beers and some loud rock and roll. I was a tad sheepish about being barred by Albert and Marino, but being barred from the Station wasn't a rare occurrence, although it was a first for me. I was optimistic that either the dust would have settled or they'd have learned I wasn't the instigator. I could almost feel my halo appear as I walked into the pub. I was sure I could talk them around if there was still a problem. Surely.

The first thing I saw when I got inside was Bon ironing his red satin bib-'n'-brace overalls on the bar. His dress sense hadn't improved much since the Valentines, it would seem. But, you know, it was *Bon Scott*. Bon was always very, very particular about his appearance, his clothes and, more than anything else, his hair. Vince Lovegrove, Bon's singing partner in the Valentines, told me that Bon always wanted a fringe, and it had to be dead straight across his forehead. Bon's answer was to wash his hair, get the fringe just right and then fasten it down in place with sticky tape to dry dead straight. It was probably the only thing about Bon Scott that was dead straight.

As I watched Bon do his ironing, I heard a voice. An unhappy voice. 'You're barred, you little prick.' It was Albert.

'Here we go again,' I thought. It appeared I'd be back out on the footpath, on my arse again, very smartly. A push and shove began, and I managed to get a nice shot in on Albert during the skirmish. But I was getting the bum's rush from Albert when Tana Douglas stepped in. Tana was the tallest of the lot of us, which helped. She explained to a very heated licensee that I was in the band.

'That,' she said, pointing to my bass rig on the stage, 'is his gear.'

Tana was a 'top sort' as the Prahran vernacular went in those days, so she managed to charm her way around the irate owners. I don't think I have ever seen a more attractive roadie in all my years of playing. And she seemed dead keen on Malcolm. Tana said that if Albert wanted the band to play, he'd better let me stay.

'Well, he can stay,' said Albert, 'but he better fucking keep in line.'

Incidentally, this is probably how the urban myth began that I met and joined AC/DC after seeing them at the Station, having trouble with the bouncers, a fight breaking out and Bon Scott and my mate Steve McGrath coming to my rescue. Sure, there was a shred of truth to that, but it wasn't the full story.

Peace now made with Albert, I made my way over to Bon, who I was extra keen to meet. He looked me up and down and then he spoke his first words to me. 'What are you like at ironing, mate?' Off he went and ordered two beers and two Scotches.

'Now, you're talking,' I said to myself. 'I'm drinking with Bon Scott!'

He collected the drinks, walked right past me and sat down with the best-looking girl in the place.

I was there with my mates Graham Kennedy and Micky Smith. I'd filled in the guys on my state of play with the band,

and asked them along for moral support and also to get their take on AC/DC. It's hard to now imagine the band as a quartet, with Malcolm on bass, but it worked a treat. Then again it was the first time I had seen them live and it was hard not to be impressed by Bon and Angus doing their thing, particularly in a tiny pub like the Station. I didn't think of it at the time, of course, but I wish I had asked someone to take a few photos of the four-piece AC/DC live. They were really cooking. I remember Micky saying to me, 'Why the fuck do they want to change this?' I had to agree. We were all impressed by the four-piece AC/DC.

The sound at the Station was coming straight off the stage, as the band had a very small PA system, no monitor system and no lights, so it was a very spartan set up. But it was enough for me. I was keen as mustard to climb aboard after watching their first set, even if it was for only sixty bucks a week. Money didn't come into it, really; even the prospect of making money should the band become successful wasn't a factor. I was just totally into the idea of going on the road with a rock and roll band. And not just any band, either. I could tell that these guys were the real deal. There were plenty of girls looking on, too, something that was duly noted by my pals that night. I couldn't see any good reason why I shouldn't get involved with that action.

Glynis and I were still an item, sort of. She'd caught me with my hands in another girl's cookie jar, so to speak, which cast a pall over our situation. There was some world championship plate-throwing going on there for a while, but we stayed good mates and part-time bed buddies, although our cohabitation days had come to an end. Glynis had some well-founded issues with regards to trusting me, issues that sure looked like they could get a serious work-out by some of the very well-stacked young ladies who were following AC/DC. I could hear the keys to the candy store janglin'.

The first set was loud and in your face. Micky asked whether Angus was 'like that' all the time.

'What do you mean?' I asked.

'He's a bit wound up, isn't he? What is he on?'

My answer was straight down the line. 'I have absolutely no idea.'

But Micky was insistent. 'Find out what it is, will ya?'

Little did I know, but I'd be asked the same question repeatedly virtually from that day onwards. Punters couldn't get their head around Angus's energy level. I must admit he had me scratching my head, too. But Angus was manic once he hit the stage; he just exploded and didn't back off. I've always admired his intensity level—once the band fired up, he gave it everything. That was definitely the case this night at the Station.

So, come the second set, it was my turn to get up with the band. A few beers and a couple of Scotches had me well warmed up. I was feeling good about playing with the guys; the songs were no huge stretch and I'd sat through the first set, so I knew what to expect. I stepped up onto the stage and into AC/DC.

Phil greeted me with a big smile. 'Stand right there, mate,' he said, pointing with his drumstick to a spot right next to his hi-hat stand.

We started off with 'Soul Stripper', the song the 'last guy' couldn't get together, as Mal had told me. All I know about this mystery man is that he kept fucking up 'Soul Stripper'.

I thought it would go a long way to sealing the deal if 'Soul Stripper' stuck—and it did, like glue. It all felt good from the get-go. Playing bass with these guys was a buzz, but then again, if you couldn't play bass to Phil Rudd's drums and Malcolm Young's rhythm guitar, it was time to find another career path. We finished the set with what would become our closer for my entire tenure with the band: 'Baby Please Don't Go'.

We'd built up a fair head of steam by now and I got to experience the Angus Young epileptic-schoolboy spin-out for the first time, and at close range. I was stunned at how he could play so quickly, cleanly and precisely while gyrating and spinning around on the filthy Station Hotel floor. I also found out that Angus's staple diet of milk and chocolate bars, when mixed with the sweat and the schoolboy orbital action, turned the guy into a snot cyclone. Anyone on stage with him would cop a lashing, and the front rows weren't safe, either. He just let it all fly, snot and all.

I was gobsmacked; so were my pals. I spoke to Graham a few minutes after coming off the cramped stage.

'Whaddya think?'

'Mate,' he said to me, 'you have gotta do this gig!'

ϟ

The motivating factor for my recruitment had to be that Malcolm never saw himself as a bass player. As we'd all come to learn, there's not too many guitar players that can set up a tune like Mal; to me he ranks with the Stones' Keith Richards and ZZ Top's Billy Gibbons in that department. It seems strange now, but Malcolm and Angus were the unknowns to me at the time, and I certainly wasn't alone in thinking that. I knew of their big brother, George, but I didn't have any idea about Mal and Angus, and pretty much the same went for the rest of Melbourne, I guess. But that was about to change real fast. AC/DC didn't add up to much in early 1975, except they had a real vibe about them and people were starting to get it, although there were some raised eyebrows about the 'kid' in the school uniform.

I found out that Michael Browning had insisted on checking me out that night at the pub. I became aware that if I hadn't met with Michael's approval that would have been it—no gig. Michael's main concern was the visual side of things: did I suit the band's image? And how tall was I? Or should I say, in AC/DC's case, how short was I? Like I said, I felt like a giant among men in AC/DC. That's something that AC/DC had in common with our blueprint band, the Rolling Stones: we were all 'vertically challenged'.

So Malcolm had invited me to the gig not only so I could check out the band live and jam with them, but for Michael to measure me up. When Mal finally introduced me to Michael, he said, 'This is the guy I told you about.' No name, no shaking hands, no polite introduction at all. Michael had a decent look at me, looked at Mal and nodded. That was it, I was in. I didn't really expect any great fanfare, but a handshake or a 'welcome aboard' would have been nice. Still, had to beat the public service. Michael gave me the nod and I *was* in, and that was the way it worked from then on: decisions were made without a lot of input from either me or Phil Rudd.

Back in those early days the band was certainly not a democratic beast. I immediately felt like it was Malcolm's band—as Ralph had warned me—and the decisions regarding our career seemed to happen by osmosis, as far as I was concerned.

Regardless of the politics, that night was a revelation for me. I could actually see a chance to have a serious crack at the music business with a band that played well and had the same tastes as I did. The Stones, ZZ Top—their *Tres Hombres* is still a favourite album of mine—Chuck Berry, Little Richard, these were all band staples, and they were right up my alley.

The punters at the Station were known to be a discerning bunch musically. It was an interesting cross-section of hippies, drunks and curious music fans who checked out AC/DC that night. There was a bit of 'what the fuck is this all about?' with the schoolboy carry-on, particularly from the crew that was enticed to the gig by Bon's presence in the band. It was a rather large leap from dope smoking and lentil soup with Fraternity to Bon's new life in AC/DC. But Bon was far better suited to wailing and causing mayhem in a gritty, bluesy rock and roll outfit than he would have been with the brown-rice brigade. It had to be a whole lot more fun than living up in the Adelaide Hills wearing caftans, for fuck's sake!

After my first night out with the guys at the Station Hotel, I opened my account with the ladies as an eager rock-and-roller, even before I had struck a blow with the band at an official gig. We all headed back to the Lansdowne Road house where I became the willing filling in a 'rock and roll sandwich'. I had met my two new female pals at the Station. They were there to see AC/DC and took a shine to me almost immediately (well, immediately after it became apparent that I was likely to be the new bass player). We all retired to Chateau AC/DC for an après-gig drink or ten. I supplied a bottle of

Johnnie Walker and some Coke (that capital C is intentional), which endeared me to the troops no end.

Jennie and Sandy (not their real names), my bedroom bookends, were well known to the band. They were part of the coterie that kept such struggling groups as AC/DC alive and kicking. They were good sports, keen to lend a hand (or any other part of their bodies) to help out a band member in need. They were quite happy to be christened 'band-aids' and proved to be very welcome company back at the ranch after the gig at the Station. I was feeling good, the gig had gone well and I was being welcomed into the clan. Bon wasn't there, though. As would become the norm, he had split after the show to be with his then girlfriend Judy King, a very tidy young thing.

Anyway, a few drinks in and I was all warm and fuzzy from the Johnnie Walker and the attention I was receiving from the girls. It was starting to dawn on me just how good it might be playing in a rock and roll band. I decided that it would be wise to adjourn to a more private setting, so I was off to Phil's room with one of the girls. For the life of me I can't remember who was the first cab off the rank, or how the choice was made, but after a very short while we were joined by my other new chum. 'Thanks for leaving me out there,' she sniffed. 'I thought we were together.' I was sure warming to the band lifestyle.

We all became close personal friends during the later part of the evening and early morning. It was the start of a steep learning curve for me; there is a real art to keeping two ladies happy in the sack, I can tell you. And it was a load of fun learning the ropes. Luckily, I seemed to pick it all up fairly quickly. A tip here for the young players: don't get too keen too early, take your time and be aware that you can always catch a breather, if necessary, when the ladies get involved with each other, which they invariably do. I even had a little nap during proceedings, during which the girls kept their motors running until I came back to life and came good again, so to speak. It's amazing what you can achieve when you are motivated.

Actually, this wasn't my first time in such a fortunate situation. Trial and error is an important part of any *ménage à trois*, and there was a time when I had two willing 'research assistants' happy to come back to the Hilton and help me out. But the trouble was my mother paid an unexpected visit—nothing is more mortifying than being caught on the job by your mum. After an embarrassing pause, all I could do was take a deep breath and make the appropriate introductions.

'Mum,' I said, 'I'd like you to meet—' and just at that point my second friend's head popped out from under the covers.

My dear mum did a classic double take then asked: 'Mark Whitmore Evans—just how many have you got in there?'

Chapter 3

Blowing up on *Countdown*

The appearance of the band was changing, thankfully, around the time I joined. I don't know who pushed the glam rock thing, but that's how the band started out: all platform boots and silk. It was suggested that I wear a red cap along with a red satin jacket that appeared from who knows where. When George Young was filling in on bass he wore the red cap and it was put to me that if I wore it 'no one would know the difference'. I chose not to go with the cap—I've never been completely at home with headgear—but the pain-in-the-arse red satin jacket hung around, though only for a brief period, thank god.

I think it became clear that if we stuck with the glam angle, no matter how watered down, there would be an eventual culture clash with the Sharpies, skinheads and general roughnuts that made up much of our following in the Melbourne beer barns. It got pretty uneasy at times even without the satin gear, but if you were wearing that type of garb in a pub you had to be able to take care of yourself, or were crazy, or both. It wasn't a conscious decision or a directive from 'above' to change our look, we just drifted away from it and ended up in something that was more at home with the band's sound and image. How could you be a street punk in satin for chrissakes? AC/DC's early look never gelled with what I was hearing. I heard this loud, dirty, bluesy rock band, yet I'd open my eyes and all I could see was silk, satin and platform shoes. Fuckin' hell!

I was told that Malcolm had been a big fan of Marc Bolan, from T-Rex, so maybe an embarrassed finger can be pointed in that direction. Herm Kovac, the drummer from the Ted Mulry Gang, an Albert Productions stable mate, played in a pre-AC/DC band with Malcolm that operated under the very ill-conceived name Velvet Underground, with all due apologies to Lou Reed and Co. Herm swears he saw a photo of Marc Bolan up on Malcolm's bedroom wall at the Young family home in Sydney's Burwood. But in Malcolm's defence, Herm did stress it was 'only a small photo'. (In fact, our first TV show in the UK was on Marc Bolan's 'comeback special', where we played one hundred per cent live, a fact of which I'm very proud.)

My first official AC/DC gig was on Thursday, 20 March 1975 at the Waltzing Matilda Hotel on Heatherton Road, Springvale, an outer south-eastern suburb of Melbourne. It was the standard beer-barn gig, two sets from 10 pm to finish by 11.30 pm. The Waltzing Matilda was a massive place, part of a hotel/motel complex, with a room capacity of 1200. This was the type of gig that would become the lifeblood of AC/DC in Melbourne. Big outer suburban pubs like this featured two live bands on Thursdays, Fridays and Saturdays.

It cost two dollars to get in and the main attraction was that you could keep drinking until 11.30 pm, unlike the normal pub closing time of 10 pm.

I was a bit nervous that night but once we were tuned up and hit the stage it was all guns blazing. In essence all I had to do was fit in with Malcolm and Phil and they were rock-solid from the get-go. I really was flying first class with those two. When Bon wasn't singing or trying to scope out some après-gig action in the crowd, he was very supportive. He'd sashay up to me during a song and say, 'Going all right, Mike.' Maybe I was, but I was also looking forward to Bon getting my name right. (Then again, maybe he knew something I didn't: the first load of gold records I received had the name 'Mike Evans' inscribed on them.) On stage, Bon and Angus were bouncing off each other and it was something to see from my perspective, absolute dynamite.

During that first gig we played the entire *High Voltage* album with a few covers thrown in, including 'Jailhouse Rock' and the Stones' 'Jumpin' Jack Flash'. We also did an extended, and I do mean extended, version of 'Baby Please Don't Go' to close the night. The crowd was a reasonable size, with plenty of rough local blockheads looking on. But the crowds in those early days didn't really know what to make of us, I'm sure. The usual reaction was subdued and encores were a very rare occurrence. We certainly didn't get one that night at the Waltzing Matilda, but we did get paid $250. Not a bad night's work.

The television show *Countdown* was incredibly influential in breaking bands, and its guiding light and host, Ian 'Molly'

Meldrum, most definitely took us under his wing. Over time he'd push us as hard as he ever pushed anyone. Molly and Bon already knew each other, but it was the first time that the rest of the band, me included, had any dealings with him. Molly was a very flamboyant character, full of beans and evidently always up for a good time—I'm pretty sure nothing's changed over the years. He struck me as this big ball of nervous energy. We didn't mix much socially with Molly—it was pretty apparent that we moved in different circles—but whenever our paths did cross he was guaranteed to be good company. Molly aided and abetted our progress to the point of being the ringleader in inciting what he called a 'riot' in Adelaide at a New Year's Eve show when the power was cut on us for going overtime.

Countdown was a national program, running for an hour early Sunday evening on ABC TV, which was the only truly national network in the 1970s. If you appeared semi-regularly on *Countdown* at the very least it assured you of half a hit record *and* the potential to tour nationally as a known act. *Countdown* is historically known for breaking Abba—whether that's a claim to fame or not, I'll leave to you to judge. Those Swedes had some pretty wacky, spaced-out stage outfits too, so looking back at Mal's early stage gear, maybe we had more in common with them than I first realised.

Countdown was promoted as a 'live' show, and it was in as much as it was taped before a live audience, in the running order you saw on air, so if there were any gaffes they pretty much stayed. It was a mixture of film clips supplied by record companies and acts in the studio miming to a backing track—but with live vocals to give the impression it was happening then and there. It all sounds a tad squeaky now but I can't stress how important the show was for us. It was a massive shortcut and indispensable for anyone hoping to make it big in Australia. I don't know what was done behind the scenes to ensure the support AC/DC received, if in fact there was any lobbying done on our behalf, but without *Countdown* it's debatable whether we would ever have risen to the top.

I spent my first Saturday afternoon in the band at the ABC studios in Ripponlea, not far from the Prahran Hilton, taping my debut *Countdown* appearance, which aired on Sunday, 23 March 1975. I had done just two gigs with the band at this stage. It would be the first of many *Countdowns*, personally memorable for marking my debut, but more memorable for Bon's antics. We were performing 'Baby Please Don't Go', the single that was currently doing pretty well.

We rehearsed the song and the crew set up their shots and so on. We were the opening act on the show. The studio was well equipped, being government-funded, but primitive by today's standards. After a couple of run-throughs they herded in the kids and the cameras started rolling. Talking of primitive, some of the young ladies in the audience could get very primal, too. We launched into the song's intro . . . and Bon was nowhere to be seen. The crew was in a panic—where the fuck was Bon? We hadn't seen him for some time, either. After what seemed like an eternity, but was probably only a matter of seconds, he appeared in full drag: schoolgirl's tunic, make-up and an outrageous plaited wig, carrying a giant rubber mallet—god knows why—all the while puffing on a cigarette. A hell of a look.

As for the rest of us, we were all trying to keep straight faces and look as cool as a rock band should, but it was bloody hard. Angus was particularly jumpy and jittery, but Bon was busy being himself, despite the fact he was dressed as the schoolgirl from hell. In a period of music that was noted for such pompous, puffed-up acts as Queen, Yes and King Crimson, here we were, a scruffy Aussie rock band, starring a schoolboy guitarist and his dirty sidekick dressed up as a schoolgirl, flashing his knickers on national TV. That was my introduction to performing on television. It'll do me fine, thanks.

My father Pat was born in Sydney so I'd always felt a strong connection to the harbour city. As a preschooler I would spend hour upon hour drawing and painting pictures of the Sydney Harbour Bridge, literally hundreds of them, and always with a beautiful, clear blue sky and bright sunshine that highlighted the ferries on the harbour. I had visited Sydney twice as a teenager, road trips with a bunch of pals, so it was a red-letter day for me to hit the road with AC/DC for the first time and head north to Sydney.

It was early May 1975 and the right time to introduce the new AC/DC line-up to the Youngs' hometown. I'd only been in the band for six weeks but had already picked up that Mal and Angus weren't a hundred per cent comfortable living in Melbourne. They definitely missed Sydney and the comforts of their Burwood family HQ. But when Michael Browning became AC/DC's white knight and saved the band from extinction it was a forgone conclusion that they'd be based in Melbourne for the immediate future. It was Mal and Angus's first time living away from home, so any trip back was greeted with about as much excitement as the Young brothers would let slip—but blink and you missed it.

Our schedule was always brisk, but this working week in Sydney was a hectic one. Michael tried to pack in as many shows as possible. The reasoning behind this was twofold. The obvious one was to help build the band's following via live shows, thus promoting *High Voltage*, which was just starting to grow legs on the back of radio airplay of 'Baby Please Don't Go' and our *Countdown* appearances. The other was a little more mercenary. Michael's contract with the band stated that he would float our expenses, pay the band members a wage and pick up all income. The equation was simple: more gigs maximized income.

Our sojourn started on a Monday night, 5 May, at what would become our Sydney power base, the infamous Bondi Lifesaver. The Swap, as it was known (shortened from 'Bondi Wifeswapper'), was *the* club in Sydney in the mid-1970s, for punters and players. It was the place to meet up with pals from other bands after gigs with the plan of getting whacked and picking up a playmate for the night. Everything was available at the Swap—for a price, of course—or until your band got hot, and then you didn't pay for anything.

The venue featured a very long bar on the right-hand side as you entered, next to the stage. There was a raised restaurant area and kitchen at the back; the centrepiece was a large tank holding an impressive display of tropical fish, the owner's pride and joy. There was also a large beer garden opposite the bar, so there were plenty of places to hide away and get up to some 'dirty deeds'.

We were booked to play the Lifesaver four nights on the trot, Monday through Thursday. Judging by the crowd (or lack thereof) on the first night, we didn't mean much to Sydneysiders. There were probably fifty people through the club during the entire evening, and it was a long, long night as we played four sets, each forty-five minutes long. We were on stage for three hours every night. We had the tunes from *High Voltage* but little else, so we just winged it and played anything that came to mind. The Monday night opening set was just a jam to about half a dozen people, played at a typically ear-shattering volume, as was (and still is) the AC/DC way. We blasted the brave half a dozen into the beer garden quick smart. Once they were outside, fuck 'em; they could stay out there.

At the end of the first set the manager of the club, a tiny blonde ball of energy, greeted us. And she was going ballistic. There was some Olympic-standard stick coming our way; she was swearing with an intensity that I have never heard since. 'You fuckin' little pricks, who the fuck do you think you are, you fuckin' cocksuckers?' And so on. You get the drift. We had driven her only customers outside; they had the shits and so did she, big time.'YOU FUCKIN' COCKSUCKERS!!!!'

So ended our first set at the Lifesaver. Only another fifteen sets to go. Apparently the tropical fish didn't survive our four-night residency either.

What did make it a bit easier was the Squire Inn, where we were staying. It was just across the car park from the Swap, so you could nip back to the room to take care of any pressing business between sets. Bon, Phil and myself were sharing one room for the first and last time. Bon pulled seniority and got the double bed; I scored a single with the best view of the TV. Mal and Angus were firmly ensconced at home in Burwood, which was a wise move. They took the chance to get fed properly, have their clothes washed, new school uniforms made . . . You know, all the normal domestic creature comforts.

It was a long week with some seriously long nights. Any remaining innocence I may have had was blown straight out the Squire Inn windows, as I learned about how to keep my energy levels up. I was curious about all this sniffing going on, and, hey, what's that white powder? It didn't take long to work it out. Gentlemen, start your engines! Mine was in overdrive.

Once some punters started coming through the door, the Lifesaver tenure and general vibe improved. It's amazing what a steady flow of cash can do to a club owner, even one who is grieving over the sudden and traumatic loss of their beloved tropical fish. We were still very much on the bottom rung in Sydney but we could feel our position improving. Over time, more punters, more airplay and more *Countdowns* meant, well, more punters, more airplay and more *Countdowns*.

Those four nights at the Lifesaver were followed by double gigs on Friday and Saturdays, with an all-ages gig early at a youth club (who the fuck knows where, but at least there weren't any tropical fish) followed by a later pub gig. Welcome to Sydney! Sniff, sniff.

I was settling in with the band, taking the lead from the other guys, not being exactly anti-social towards other bands, but pretty much ignoring them as they didn't seem to matter much, if at all. It wasn't bordering on contempt; most of the time it was actually fully-blown contempt. I'm not sure this sat well with Bon's personality and he would readily seek company outside the band, keeping in touch by letter with his ex-wife Irene, his brother Graeme and close friends like Mary Walton.

Mary had a groovy clothes shop in Greville Street, Prahran, just down from the Station Hotel, and she gladly offered the friendship and sanctuary that Bon sought. It would be a lifelong relationship for him. Bon was a habitual letter writer, keeping a small circle of people close to him up to date with band news and his exploits—especially whose body he was playing with, even if it was just his own. He called these dispatches 'News from My Front'. Strangely, for such a gregarious guy, Bon's true friends seemed thin on the ground.

I met Patrick Francis Xavier Pickett on Wednesday, 4 June 1975. I know this because it happened at an AC/DC gig at the Sundowner Hotel in Geelong. Pat was living in Geelong, working at the abattoirs as a slaughterman. Pat had come along to the Sundowner that night to catch up with his good mate Bon. They had met in Adelaide while Bon was in Fraternity and Pat had been compelled to 'get out of Melbourne real quick'. Pat's term for this was 'things were getting a bit tropical'. No details were ever offered but it became known he had done one stretch and had no desire for a repeat dose of Her Majesty's hospitality. Pat was the only guy I can ever recall Bon introducing to me as 'his mate'.

We were standing at the bar at the Sundowner when Pat first spoke to me.

'Want a pig's ear, mate?'

The alarm bells started ringing pretty loudly. Here was a slaughterman with a crazy glint in his eye offering me a pig's ear. This was my first lesson in Pickett rhyming slang and the start of a true friendship that I would cherish for the rest of my days. Pat was, in fact, offering me a beer.

Pat was a praying mantis of a guy with crazy laser beam eyes, his stick figure body covered in tattoos. This was capped with a shock of prematurely thinning dark hair. His height was in striking contrast to the rest of us; he stood a good 30 centimetres taller than his new little mate, Angus. Pat by his own admission had a 'head like a hundred yards of unmade road', but I'd come to learn that this was no hindrance when it came to the ladies. He did well. I'm still mystified how the ugly fucker got away with it.

At the Sundowner Pat got stuck into the pig's ear, into several in fact, eventually pouring himself into the AC/DC bus at the end of the night. Ralph the Roadie told him that the next stop was the Freeway Gardens Motel, AC/DC's new home in North Melbourne. Pat stayed on the bus because we had, in his own words, 'a couple of good sorts on the boil'.

It was an extra large night at the Freeway Gardens. I passed out on the couch after too many pig's ears and awoke the next morning to a tennis commentary.

'Newcombe to serve for the match. Tosses the ball high in the air . . .'

I looked up from the couch. The commentary was coming from Pat, along with the actions, but without clothes. He wasn't wearing a stitch of clothing, apart from a pair of odd-coloured socks. He was using a frying pan as a tennis racquet. Pat duly hit the winning serve, yelled 'Newk, you beaut!', then sent the frying pan smashing straight through the lounge room window. So far, I'd known Pat for twelve hours; I'd gotten tanked with him and saw him hurl a frying pan through a window, impersonating John Newcombe at Wimbledon, naked. We were off to a good start.

Pat looked at me and said, 'I'm going to jump in the Eiffel Tower and give my Yogi Bear a lemon squash 'cos it's a bit nine-thirty.'

I've been laughing ever since. I leave it up to you to do the translation.

Later that morning we were back on the bus, bound for a four-night residency at the Largs Pier Hotel in Adelaide. We dropped Pat at Kensington railway station and waved him off. We arrived at the Largs Pier Hotel some twelve hours later, to be told we had four rooms booked, three triples and one single.

'Oh, and your lighting director got here first so he took the single room.'

Now, this was odd. We didn't have a lighting director; we didn't even have any fucking lights. Where we asked, could we find our lighting director?

'He's in the bar having a counter meal.'

We all marched off to the bar to be greeted by Pat's bony butt bent over the pool table. He smacked the eight ball straight into a corner pocket and addressed the entire bar: 'That one went in rubbing its arse.'

We didn't have a new lighting director; we had much more. We had Pat Pickett on the team. Pat started out as resident court jester doubling as security for Angus, but went on to become our stage roadie, protector and social secretary. He became a legendary figure in the Australian live music scene, the guy you wanted to run your crew; an unconventional, eccentric, oddly reassuring and efficient character to have around when the shit hit the fan; a bloke who could be extremely volatile but always entertaining. Maybe it's a blessing that Pat was the only one of Bon's mates I met. I'm not sure I would have survived another.

When I joined AC/DC, their transport was an ex-Greyhound bus that had been converted to suit the band's needs. The back half had been partitioned off to allow for stage gear and PA, while the front was set apart for band and crew. When I signed on and for some time after, the bus was in the repair shop, which was a constant source of mirth for the band and a strain on the chequebook of Michael Browning's management company, Trans Pacific Management.

TPM did sound quite grand, but it was simply a company put together by Michael and his then business partner Bill Joseph to create a much-needed infrastructure for the band once it was repatriated to its current HQ in East St Kilda. Michael and Bill created the lifeline that was desperately needed by the band; without their support, both financial and logistic, my instinct tells me that the AC/DC story may have been a lot shorter than it now is—if there was a story to be told at all.

Browning's introduction to AC/DC came when he booked the band for the Hard Rock Café as they passed through Melbourne from Sydney, en route to Adelaide for what were surely low-paying gigs. He must have been impressed and struck up a relationship with Malcolm; in fact it was Malcolm who sent an SOS to Michael when the band's then manager, Denis O'Loughlin, hit the wall and left them stranded in Adelaide. Michael dived in and, from what I gleaned, saved the band's arse.

The lifeline thrown to the band by TPM had many immediate benefits. When AC/DC shifted to Melbourne, it was the core of a band, just Malcolm, Angus and Bon; no other band members survived the new regime. That's what made Michael's decision to rescue the band a massive leap of faith—to put together the package to repatriate an act that was essentially rudderless. There would be plenty of angst to come, but never, ever would it be a dull ride.

The new model provided by Michael was this: all members of the band were put on a wage of sixty dollars a week, with Malcolm and Angus having fifteen a week deducted to cover some previous debts. The band was housed in the place on Lansdowne Road, which was close to the city, the Hard Rock Café and the TPM office and agency. To round it out TPM supplied the PA and crew (there were no lights, they would come later with a PA upgrade) and last, but certainly not least, that blue Greyhound bus, just the thing to convey 'this band of vagabonds and thieves', as Angus referred to us. So it was all there: money, a home, gear, crew, transport, management, agent and, the essential thing for any band, a constant flow of gigs, many and varied, all organised by Michael. And there was Browning's inner-city venue, the Hard Rock Café, to use as a base to grow a following. That's the rock-solid set-up I was thrown into in March '75.

Phil was parachuted into the same deal a month earlier, well after the first Australian album, *High Voltage*, was recorded. Bon preceded Phil and I by a good few months and was, of course, involved up to his neck in the band's debut album, clutching his schoolbooks full of handwritten 'dirty ditties'. It was a very different band to the outfit that had made its public debut in Sydney on New Year's Eve 1973, playing a few originals and a bunch of Stones and Chuck Berry covers.

But back to the bus . . . It was a temperamental piece of machinery. When I first heard Mal refer to it, it was with a fair bit of consternation. He said, 'I think we've fuckin' pushed it further than we've ridden in the thing.' It didn't do much for my confidence, but after a few weeks Uncle Gus, as it was to be known, was back in commission.

Although I have some fine memories of our ride, I think the thing was jinxed from the start. One problem was trying to stay warm, quite a challenge in a bus that didn't have any heating. I'd do whatever was necessary to beat the cold. While travelling east from Melbourne to Gippsland one night, I brought along a couple of sisters for company. Until that night we were just good mates, but with a few drinks on board and the fact that it was very, very cold on the way home—well, before I knew it I wasn't feeling so cold and we were all on very friendly terms. Pat Pickett referred to it as 'Mark's Sister Sandwich', and it's highly recommended, a hell of a lot of fun, but I had to be sneaky. It was one thing to luck out like that but I'm sure the ladies didn't want the whole bus to know. It would have caused a riot. I'll keep their names private here, being the gentleman that I am, although I do know that at least one sister holds very fond memories of that journey. She recalled the experience almost 'blow by blow' a few years later during a conversation we had at a party. Her recall was excellent, by the way.

Still, you could really freeze your arse off in that blue fucker of a bus. I swear, hypothermia was always lurking just around the next bend. Early one Monday morning, approaching Goulburn on the way to Sydney, ice formed on the inside of the side windows—it was like being trapped in a giant beer cooler.

We would do a gig on a Sunday night in Melbourne, Ralph and Tana would pack the gear and we would hit Highway 31 to Sydney. Only Ralph the Roadie would drive the bus. He'd drive all night, stopping only for diesel and coffee, or at least what I thought was regular coffee. What started as a 'quick pit stop' got corrupted to a 'quick piss stop' somewhere along Highway 31. Ralph would order a coffee, go for a 'quick piss stop', get the coffee and expect everyone to be back on the bus to get rollin'. There was no food, no snacks, just Ralph and his 'coffee' and miles of highway.

I was amazed at Ralph's long-haul bus-driving prowess. Ralph would mention his 'truck driver's friend' and boast about how 'bright-eyed and bushy-tailed' he was during the overnighters, while the rest of us were catching some shut-eye. Ralph was either Superman or he had some serious artificial encouragement. It just goes to show how naive I was in early '75; I actually thought it was just coffee that kept him going.

Naivety disappears very quickly once you hit the road as part of a rock band. And hit it I did; from the time I joined in March to the time we left for the UK, a year and a bit later, we didn't stop touring. I can't even recall how many gigs we played in that time, although I'm sure plenty of AC/DC-spotters could give me an exact figure. More than 300 for sure.

We'd always stop to see the Ettamogah bunyip. This was at Malcolm's absolute insistence and something I would also insist on in my later bands. The Ettamogah bunyip was to be found just north of Albury, on the border of New South Wales, at Ettamogah (no surprise there). On an overnighter heading north we would hit Ettamogah around 3 am but that would not stop Mal from rousing all his fellow travellers out of their slumber. We'd gather in front of a cyclone-wire enclosed booth in the car park and wait for Mal to pop twenty cents into the slot.

You looked through the cyclone fence into a small, scungy lagoon in which the legendary bunyip resided. Then the twenty cents would start working its magic, summoning the bunyip to appear, but not before a series of unearthly sounds squeaked out of some real cheap, crappy speakers. A few feet away the stinking water would bubble and the bunyip would slowly start to rise, growling.

The bunyip looked like a large frog; the dumbest, goofiest frog you could imagine. But what made it ludicrous was that someone had put a lot of work into the enterprise, trying to make it genuinely scary. It was way too clunky to be anything but hilarious. And that's what appealed to Mal and Angus, every time. They would be in absolute hysterics, which would get me going too. It was a side of the Youngs that was infectious, funny as fuck and unfortunately rarely on display.

We had some mammoth overnight journeys on the bus. We played Whyalla in South Australia one Saturday night, the crew packed the gear, and off we drove the 400 kilometres back to Adelaide, then straight through to Melbourne, another 600 kilometres, to do a show Sunday afternoon at Victoria Park. We were late but the show still went on. I will admit the show was a little less 'high voltage' than normal. I was absolutely knackered, before, after and during that gig, but Bon and Angus were going for it, pulling out all stops. I just shook my head; I had no idea how they could keep on keeping on. Perhaps, though, it was the effect Victoria Park had on me—after all, it was the home of the Collingwood Football Club, the archenemy of my team, Carlton. The last time I'd been there I ended up with a few stitches in my head. I wish I could tell you I was in a massive brawl and sound like a real tough guy but the truth is I got brained by a little old lady who hit me with her umbrella. Those Collingwood biddies can be rough.

The first time I ever saw snow was from inside the bus. We were on our way back into Melbourne after a country gig and woke to Ralph yelling, 'What the fuck is going on?' Initially I thought he might have had a little extra truck-driver's friend and lost it, but no, we slid to a halt, no mean feat in a bus full of gear, band and crew. It was snowing outside. That was it, with a whoop and a holler Mal and Angus were out of the bus like a couple of kids, having a ball.

They could be contradictory buggers, those two. The Youngs could be morose, grumpy, sullen and generally not too much fun to be around—but now here I was watching the two of them bounce around in the snow (or at least what passes for snow in Australia) like kids on holiday. I was pissing myself laughing, too; their mood was infectious. But once they were back in the bus, the moment passed and it was back to moody normal, like nothing had happened. Still, it was refreshing to see them let their guard slip for a moment. When those guys were on and enjoying themselves it was party time and they were great company. I just wish I had seen it more often.

In between all this road action, we connected with *Countdown* again. They went to the extent of packaging and producing two film clips for us, outdoor shoots at that. I'm sure they must have done similar promotion for other acts, but for the life of me I can't recall one. Not that I was much aware of other music at the time: I was most definitely an ignoramus, a cheeky shortarse with a face full of pimples to boot. I can thank the *Countdown* make-up people for the decent lather of zit-hiding foundation they applied every time we went on the show. I also thank my lucky stars I was in an up-and-coming rock and roll band, otherwise I never would have got laid.

Actually, I can also thank *Countdown* for providing our passport photos. At one recording they had a guy come in and take our photos, which were used for our passports and for the inner sleeve of the TNT album. Look closely and you'll see that Bon is wearing a bow tie, but no shirt. What passes for an acceptable passport photo has certainly changed since then.

Countdown came up with the idea of putting us on the back of a truck driving down Swanston Street, Melbourne's main drag, to promote our song 'It's a Long Way to the Top'. That happened on a Monday morning around the time of the release of our album *TNT*, which reached number two in the charts in January 1976. What struck me was how quiet Swanston Street was; looking at the video it seems like a country town. Now, Melbourne was certainly not New York, Paris or Rome—and, thankfully, it never will be—but it was a city of well over two million people. Strange.

Anyway, there we were, courtesy of *Countdown*, on the back of a truck trundling down my hometown's main street with three members of the Rats of Tobruk Pipe Band on board. Initially I felt a tad sheepish about the whole enterprise but once we got going and Bon started to ham it up, it became great fun. I mean, how serious could you be when you're on the back of a truck with three pipers, a guitarist dressed up as a schoolkid and a singer wrestling with bagpipes?

The flat-bed truck was loaded up with a sound system for playback, so we would have some idea what the fuck was going on. But when the sound crew cranked up the audio to the required AC/DC level, the poor pipers nearly fell off the back of the truck. We'd forgotten they were 'civilians' and could have used a little heads-up as to what to expect. The Rats of Tobruk had pulled a sly one on us, anyway: two of the three so-called pipers were moonlighting drummers, the shifty fuckers. As we rolled along, I took great pride in telling the guys in the band that I was born at the Royal Women's Hospital, just a couple of hundred metres down the road. In true AC/DC fashion everyone was suitably underwhelmed; no surprises there.

The onlookers were bemused; there was a pretty strong whiff of 'what the fuck is going on here?' and 'who the fuck are these clowns?' in their reactions. But we could handle ourselves, so we just kept rolling and playing. After three times up and down Swanston Street we moved on to Melbourne's piss-poor excuse for a city square, where we ran through the song a few times with a static set-up. None of this footage made it into the clip—why bother when the back of the truck stuff was so good? The silk and satin glam-rock glad rags were well gone by now, incidentally, although Mal might have sneaked in a pair of knee-high boots for the occasion. (Funny—I'm sitting here writing this piece wearing a Wrangler denim cowboy shirt and a pair of Levis, the same kind of gear I was wearing on the back of the truck.)

Countdown also put together a video for our song 'Jailbreak'. That was another location shoot, in a quarry in the western Melbourne suburb of Sunshine. It was an elaborate production for those days, featuring a facade of a prison and its main gates. The script, such as it was, required Bon and Angus to burst through the gates and make their escape, with Mal and me dressed as coppers, on their tail, firing away.

They also set up a group shot and perched us atop a heap of rather unsteady boulders, while a bunch of explosions went off behind us. All the while the crew was yelling, 'DON'T REACT TO THE BOMBS!' and we responded as one with an equally loud: 'FUCK OFF!' Not reacting took some doing, let me tell you—not just because of the noise, which was deafening, but due to the heat coming off the charges, which was intense. Every time a blast went up this searing wave of heat hit us. I could actually hear my hair crackling away after each blast, a sort of a mega split-end treatment. Try keeping your balance on some shifting rocks several metres in the air while getting *your* backside fried.

In between shots, I had a good look at some of the so-called 'bombs' that were set off during the shoot. Basically they were large plastic orange juice bottles full of petrol, which had been loaded into a thick metal tube, like a miniature cannon. BOOM! Large tongues of flame, heat and a load of crap went up into the air when they were set off, and we shuddered as one. Can't recall there being a safety officer on the shoot, either.

Angus was particularly concerned by one of the final shots. It involved an extra-large orange juice bottle that blasted open the prison gates. I guess it worked because shit went everywhere and Bon and Angus made their break through what remained of the flaming prison gates. Bon ran straight through—why do singers always get to go first?—with Angus scampering after him, a very concerned young escapee in a pair of pyjamas, which didn't offer much protection from the remnants of the burning prison facade. Mal and I then came through the gates after them in hot pursuit, packing a couple of handguns. And they were real ones too, six-shot revolvers and as heavy as hell. (Memo to self: make sure to never, ever get pistol-whipped.) We weren't given any formal training, it was a case of just load 'em up and let 'em rip. It was a very cool experience to be able to blast off a few rounds, even if we were only shooting blanks.

There was also a sub-machine gun on the set, which ran off compressed air and gave out a very impressive muzzle flash, but was a bugger to hang on to. For one scene, the crew wired me up with the compressed air tube running up the sleeve of my police coat and then down the leg of the ample pair of trousers they'd given me to wear. When I fired the machine gun the air tube went nuts inside my suit; it was like having an electric snake loose in your clothes. So there I was, hanging on to this machine gun for dear life while a rubber python was thrashing around inside my pants. Not your average day at the office, let me tell you.

Countdown really went for it with the 'Jailbreak' shoot. They got Bon back the next day and wired him up with exploding blood capsules for the big finale, where he sings: 'And he made it out . . . with a bullet in his back.' As tame as it now looks, at the time it was a big deal, and the video definitely gave us a massive boost. It was well worth all the hassles of the shoot.

We also did some miles around the time of the 'Jailbreak' video shoot. We were doing a run of shows in Adelaide at the Largs Pier Hotel, Thursdays through to Sundays. Our schedule was tight, but Albert Productions, the family company that guided the recording careers of AC/DC, the Angels, Rose Tattoo and many others, insisted that we complete a video for the song 'High Voltage', with some studio 'live shots' to complement footage that was shot at Festival Hall in

Melbourne—and also do another, separate clip for 'Jailbreak'. All this years before MTV was invented.

It was decided that we would do the clips in Sydney on a Friday, during the run at Largs Pier Hotel. The big problem was the 1427 kilometres that separated Adelaide and Sydney (that's a shade under 900 miles, people). We were doing two sets a night, ending very late, over the four nights. So it was decided that we'd get up real early in Adelaide on Friday, fly to Sydney, shoot two music videos and be back to start our first set by 8 pm. No problem. Yet.

However, our early-morning flight from Adelaide was via Melbourne. It didn't seem like a huge issue: thirty minutes on the ground and off again. But Melbourne was fogged in, so we were diverted to Tasmania, a further 600 kilometres south. Then we flew back up to Melbourne, fucked around a bit there, flew to Sydney (another 800 kilometres) and finally made it to the studio for the shoot just before 2 pm. We did the filming, raced back out to Sydney Airport for the direct flight back to Adelaide—thank Christ—and made show time of 8 pm. Easy.

Yep, just another day at the coal face. I can't recall any bellyaching from the band about the workload; we just got on with things. We'd flown over 4300 kilometres, had a few drinks in four different states, shot two music videos and then performed two sets of high-voltage rock and roll in the same city we'd left at six that morning. It really was a long way to the top.

Our big blue bus would eventually die—or pretend to die—in Canberra. It was dumped at the airport, much to Michael Browning's chagrin, I'm sure. We jumped on a plane and I have absolutely no recollection what happened to all our gear. Ralph was left to take care of that, and he was great at cleaning up the messes left behind by the band, which I can tell you could be a huge and thankless task. I often think that life must have seemed to be repeating itself for Ralph, who was with Bon in the Fraternity days, travelling all over England in, yes, a customised blue ex-Greyhound bus. It must have felt like a recurring nightmare. Good old Uncle Gus still survives, too; it recently turned up on eBay. Some guy rescued it from the lock-up at Canberra Airport, fixed it up, and it now resides with Neil Smith, the very first bass player with AC/DC.

There was the odd occasion when I sought other modes of transport, with all due respect to the band bus. I once made the trip back home from Sorrento, a couple of hours south of Melbourne, in the back of a Charger, the Aussie version of a Mustang, only a little bigger. I was snuggled up with a particularly keen female fan, while her sister drove at great speed up front. She had the rear-vision mirror adjusted so that she could catch a glimpse of the goings-on in the back seat and would pass on any observations, all the while using a race caller's voice. Very entertaining. I must have been doing a reasonable job, because after a time she pulled over and asked to swap spots with her sister. Who was I to argue?

Chapter 4

Enter the Sandman

The first time I saw the inside of a recording studio was in July 1975 when I walked into the studio at Albert Productions in Sydney. Ted Albert conceived the idea of Alberts recording and promoting its own artists way back in 1964 and so Albert Productions was born as the record production side of J Albert & Son, an extremely successful music publishing company best known for its Boomerang Songsters and Boomerang brand harmonicas. The Albert family was prominent in business and social circles, to the extent that Queen Elizabeth II and Prince Philip called on Alexis Albert (Ted's father, later Sir Alexis Albert) for afternoon tea in 1954 while visiting Oz. Is that prominent enough for you?

Albert Productions would launch the Easybeats and cement Ted's relationship with George Young and Harry Vanda. Some forty-odd years later, when the Easybeats were inducted into the ARIA Hall of Fame, Harry Vanda said: 'Ted Albert is the only reason we have an industry.' On the rare occasions that Ted dropped in to the studio, he was always in a suit. He was an interesting, cordial, reserved kind of guy who was held in very high esteem by George and Harry for being able to hear a good song and/or performance. He had 'ears'.

Alberts also helped establish the careers of Billy Thorpe and the Aztecs and, in time, AC/DC. Ted Albert produced some of the early recordings himself, but now George Young and Harry Vanda made up the Alberts production team. A year earlier they'd produced the huge hit 'Evie' for Stevie Wright, and in March 1975 they produced John Paul Young's 'Yesterday's Hero', another Oz number one. They were on a roll.

The studio was on the fifth floor of Boomerang House, on King Street in Sydney, between Pitt and Castlereagh streets. It's now long gone, of course, having made way for some fancy Sydney high-rise development. It was a real rabbit warren, spread over six levels. It even had its own lift operator, who'd drop you off at the correct floor with the appropriate directions. The lift guy was known to lecture visitors if Harry Vanda had just alighted. 'You know who that was, don't you?' he'd say. 'It was Handy Andy, the world-famous songwriter from the Easybeats.'

This was where I first met Fifa Riccobono. Fifa started with Alberts in 1968 as a secretary and by the time I came on the scene it appeared (to me, anyway) that she ran the place. I liked her from the moment I met her, she made me feel very much a part of the team, and as time went on I would appreciate just how crucial Fifa was to the front office and Alberts in general. On the fifth floor at Boomerang House you turned right out of the lift, took the first door to the right and entered

Fifa's domain. I was a regular visitor to Fifa's office when we were recording. She became a great mate and was a true believer in AC/DC.

I knew from the first day that I entered Boomerang House that it was the gateway into a new, different world. Just how different it was going to be I had no idea, but like many things that were happening to the band and me it was exciting. My nerves were jangling away. But I welcomed nerves; that was part of my make-up right back to football days. Butterflies in my stomach told me I was switched on, ready to go. The trick was to harness that energy and not let it overwhelm me. Easier said than done, though. The studio was relatively new, with bits and pieces still being added, but I knew it was the spiritual home of the Easybeats, Albert Productions and the acts they worked with: Stevie Wright, TMG and, soon after, the mighty Rose Tattoo, the Angels and the Choirboys. And, of course, AC/DC.

The studio was home base for George, who was twenty-seven, and Harry, who was twenty-nine. It's a matter of Oz rock history that their songwriting partnership started way back in the early 1960s at the Villawood Migrant Hostel in western Sydney. George had emigrated with his family from Glasgow, Scotland, while Harry came from the Netherlands. Together Harry and George wrote such great songs, probably none better than the all-time classic 'Friday on My Mind'.

I was an Easybeats fan from an early age. I must have been all of eight years old when I saw them on *Bandstand*, a weekly TV music program that was required viewing at our place. I vividly recall them all suited up and ripping into 'Sorry', go-go girls go-go-ing for it behind them. They had stacks of energy and a super frontman in 'Little' Stevie Wright. They had that elusive something that sets a great band apart from the also-rans—and through an eight-year-old's eyes they were just plain exciting. What was causing quite a bit of merriment at our place was the difference in size of guitar players, and AC/DC's future producers, George and Harry. They did look comical together, particularly seeing that George held his guitar so high that it looked like an electric bow tie.

Entering that studio was the start of my musical education and I couldn't hope to be tutored by anyone better than George Young. In my time in the music business I'm yet to come across anyone more astute than George. When I met him he had done the hard yards. He'd had plenty of success with the Easybeats, particularly in England and Australia, and then went through the sobering experience of having the band that was shaping up to be world-beaters fall apart before his eyes. He brought all that hard-earned experience to the table. Put this together with his studio craft and songwriting skills, and it added up to the perfect producer for a keen rock and roll act. There was also the added bonus that his two little brothers were in the band.

George and Harry were an odd couple on a few levels, but what was most noticeable on first impression was their physical difference: George was a short, stocky, dark-haired Scotsman while Harry was blond, fair and very tall—probably the best part of a foot taller than George. Accents were all over the place, too: George's Glaswegian burr was a contrast to Harry's guttural Dutch accent and slightly fractured English. While the Dutch have never really been known for their madcap sense of humour, Harry was an exception. George and Harry were both willing to use humour to liven up proceedings when the recording atmosphere waned.

So there I was in the studio for the first time, the new boy on the block. Malcolm and Angus had recorded *High Voltage* (along with Bon), and had been in the studio before with George and Harry, most notably playing on their 1973 album *Tales of Old Grand-Daddy* under the moniker the Marcus Hook Roll Band. Phil had recorded the album *Something to Say* with Buster Brown in 1974, while Bon had a history of recording going back eight years or so, including 'My Old Man's a Groovy Old Man', the Valentines' almost-hit, written by Harry and George. But being in the studio was a new and very intense experience for me. I had a virtual crash course in recording—and there were some crashes, believe me.

The Albert studio was modest but more than serviceable. The control room looked straight through to the main recording room via the usual large glass window. The centrepiece was a grand piano. Musicians who had worked there had scrawled their signatures on one wall of the studio. Angus had drawn a self-portrait, a caricature of a leering schoolboy complete with devil horns and tail. It's since become synonymous with Angus and the band. In between the window and the mixing desk was an extremely comfortable couch that played a large part in my new nickname—the Sandman. (Check out the liner notes on the *TNT* album; there it is in black and white.) Two minutes on that couch and I was out like a light, which was a real achievement when AC/DC playbacks were ripping through the monitors a couple of feet from my head. That was one hell of a couch; I really should have bought it. It was during my time at Alberts that I mastered the art of falling asleep virtually anywhere, a handy attribute when you spend a good chunk of your life travelling, as I would over the next couple of years.

There were a couple of small, interlinked rooms off to the left of the control room. That was where we set up our gear while recording *TNT*. All the amps were in the first room, with the speakers pointed to the wall, 'miked up' and ready to go. The drums were in the other tiny room, so we could easily see Phil through the door—or at least the hole where the door had been before it was taken off.

The recording process was a fairly simple one. Basically, all the songs were written in the studio. With our live workload there wasn't any time to record or work on demo recordings. To be honest, I didn't even know what a demo was, and they didn't exist for AC/DC at that time, anyway. When Malcolm and Angus had a moment they would knock ideas and riffs together between them. Then they would sit down with George at the piano in the main room and belt the guts of the tune into shape. Some made it, some didn't.

There was a guitar riff for 'TNT' before we went into the studio—Mal talked me through it backstage at a gig in Melbourne—but let me tell you it changed a lot after George got to it. It was a classic demonstration of what George did best: simplify things. Essentially, he'd deconstruct what was already thought to be a crackerjack idea and put it through 'the process', often with Malcolm and Angus sitting either side of him at the grand piano. The riff in the case of 'TNT' got boiled down to the point where it was really movin' and a-groovin' and then everything else was built around it: intro, verse, chorus, maybe an instrumental break and so on. I had my own songwriting aspirations and ran a few things by Mal on occasion. While Mal wasn't dismissive, my not getting any riffs or bits past the post had more to do with the quality of these early efforts than anything else.

George's influence on the band can't be overstated; he really called the shots in the studio, without being overbearing. He had a great talent for getting the best out of the band—and generally that would be within the first few takes of a song. Then the fire would go out and it would be time to test-drive a new tune. That's what it was about in the studio with AC/DC—capturing the fire in a performance, and who cared if the guitars were a little out of tune? Have a listen to 'Hell Ain't a Bad Place to Be', from the *Let There Be Rock* LP: it's got all the swagger and attitude that became the AC/DC signature, but if you are a stickler for guitars being perfectly in tune, you'll feel the pain! It's a real AC/DC classic in my mind, but some producers would find that take unacceptable and want to clean it up, sanitise it. Not George.

George also had a great ability to sort through Mal and Angus's bits and pieces and put them through the songwriting/production wringer. Time was very limited so it was crucial to get on with the process. At one point, Mal asked George how a song was working out; wasn't it a bit close to previous tunes the band had recorded? George's reply has always stuck in my mind.

'But that's the band,' he said, 'that's your thing. Stick with it.'

It was a priceless piece of advice.

Once the trio had thrashed out the song around the piano, it was time for the band to work it up to speed. In the early days I was a spectator, taking it all in, because much of this would be done with George on the bass. I had no issue with this: it was how the first album was recorded, and from my vantage point, it worked beautifully with Mal and Angus on guitar and George on bass. It wasn't discussed; it was just the way it was. And what an armchair ride for me, the perfect way to learn how to operate in the studio. I would be in there kibitzing while the guys were 'brewing up a tune'. I learned as much as I could, between cups of tea, ciggie breaks and pizza.

George is recognised for his obvious songwriting expertise and production skills but what is less known is that he's an absolute legend of a bass player. George pretty much showed me the bass-playing ropes. He had a great knack for picking the perfect line, yet sometimes he'd be very busy on the bass, which can be difficult to do while still keeping the groove. It's an art. Paul McCartney played in a similar way. The bass line in the song 'High Voltage' is pretty busy for an AC/DC track but still perfect. George on bass? Very cool. As far as I'm concerned he is one of the greats.

George and Harry were a great team in the studio. It seemed to me that George was in the driver's seat most of the time, but that may have been a situation peculiar to AC/DC. Harry had some input but George was the one who got the whole thing rolling—to me it seemed like he was coaching the band. He was excellent company, too. Bon told me that when George was in Melbourne filling in on bass he was 'a party on legs'. Bon was no slouch when it came to party time, so that was high praise.

The mood in the studio while making *TNT* was pretty relaxed. I can only recall one punch-up, and even then it was on the way out of the studio, in the hallway. It had been a long day and things hadn't been going as well as they could. We were all feeling frustrated. As we were leaving, it got a bit heated between George and Angus. George told Angus that he should stop being 'such a little prima fuckin' donna'—

a pretty funny line when it's delivered in a broad Scottish accent. (Go on, try it for yourself.) It got a few sniggers. Well, that was it, Angus blew up. He was like that cartoon character Yosemite Sam, bouncing up and down. I was half expecting steam to start pouring out of his ears. He had a real foot-stamping tantrum. (I bet he was a bugger of a kid when he didn't get his way—I know I was.) Angus set upon George; there was a bit of wrestling and hair-pulling but no real damage was done.

I couldn't resist having a chuckle. I just couldn't figure out how Angus was going to beat George up. George is no giant but it's impossible for someone the size of Angus to cause any harm with his fists. Imagine being hit by an under-sized sixth-grader.

Recording the *TNT* album was a hell of an experience for me. The recording process took two weeks. A standard AC/DC studio day would commence around midday and go into the evening, breaking briefly for food, numerous cups of tea and the ubiquitous ciggies. We were there for eight hours at a stretch, maybe ten if things were booting along. The first task was to get the backing tracks down, which gave Bon time to start working on his lyrics. He would have the bare bones of a tune from which to work. Sometimes Bon would lock himself in the kitchen for some solitude, with his school exercise books full of 'dirty words', as he would call them. I personally think he was up to no good at times, too, but he managed to get away with it as only Bon could.

Bon did make a few successful escapes from his kitchen prison. We would take a break and on the way out stop by his 'cell'—but no Bon. He would resurface early the next day, the first one in the building, cheerfully talking to the office girls and making cups of tea. Basically being the charming but shifty fucker that he was, the bloke that we all loved to bits. And despite our interrogation, Bon would tell us absolutely nothing about where he'd been or what he'd been up to. Bon's good mate Pat Pickett had a saying that summed up Bon perfectly: 'He's got more moves than a tin of worms.'

The backing tracks were finalised in the first week, leaving the second week for guitar solos—Angus's favourite time, of course—and the vocals, as well as the backing vocals. This was a change from the sessions for *High Voltage*, from what I understand. Apparently time was even tighter recording the band's first album, so George and Harry sang all the backing vocals. This time Phil would help Mal with backing vocals, but that's Angus's dulcet tones supplying the first few 'oi's' on the song 'TNT', before the rest of us joined in.

Once all that was done, the project would then be left in George and Harry's care for mixing and any additives that they deemed necessary, such as percussion. The pressure was really on the band to complete all their 'parts' in two weeks. In modern terms this is an amazing feat, but it was standard operating procedure in the 1970s. It worked quite well for the *TNT* album.

The song 'It's a Long Way to the Top (If You Wanna Rock 'n' Roll)' is a great AC/DC recording, a real landmark for the band. It's a brilliant recording, full stop. It gets me every time, right from Mal's guitar intro onwards—that intro is right up there with the best, be it the Stones' 'Jumpin' Jack Flash', The Who's 'My Generation', the Kinks' 'You Really Got Me' and the rest. It's a cracker, an AC/DC trademark. Many bands have been influenced by Mal's style of intro. I know because many guitar players have taken the time to tell me.

George was instrumental, quite literally, in putting together 'It's a Long Way'. As I recall, the song started from the band playing through a couple of ideas early in a session. The tune started to take on some form and George caught on in the control room and started recording. The take that was used—and there was only one—underwent some serious editing by George. In those days of analog recording onto two-inch tape, editing was an art form. George pieced the final structure of the tune together. I saw George standing in front of the twenty-four-track Studer reel-to-reel recorder, cueing the tape up manually, finding the place to splice it, cutting a piece out with a blade and draping the excess around his neck. He was like a tailor, making the product fit perfectly.

Phil and I came in early one day and George played back what he had put together overnight. He asked us to pick what was different from the previous day. We had no idea; we couldn't spot anything. The track was seamless. I got the impression it had always been like that. I couldn't pick the edits; still can't. What I did know was that the track had a great groove. I did pick up a cymbal crash in the second chorus that shouldn't be there—it's still there, of course—but that's just one of those things you live with. Would you lose a take like that because of an errant cymbal crash? Not in a million years.

Another interesting part of recording 'It's a Long Way' was the use of bagpipes. When the idea was raised, Bon said that he'd played in a pipe band; he decided then and there he was just the guy for the job. What he neglected to tell us was that while he did play in a pipe band in Fremantle with Chick, his dad—they were known as the Coastal Scots—Bon was a drummer, not a piper. A rather large factor to leave out of the equation, don't you think?

So, with the okay of Fifa Riccobono, our indispensable go-between at Alberts, Bon was off to Bagpipes R Us in Park Street, a couple of blocks away, and then back to the studio with a set of $435 Hardy pipes. It was a very expensive purchase for a band still finding its way. Bon's omission not only presented the problem of who would play the pipes, but who'd assemble the damn thing. Now if you want a good giggle, get a bunch of Scotsmen with no previous bagpipe experience and ask them to put some bagpipes together. Watching the Youngs at work was like a Scottish Rubik's Cube, with added swearing and shouting. Perhaps it might have been an idea to hire a piper, if the track was in the right key for the bagpipes, which it wasn't.

More swearing and shouting ensued until the thing was playable. So what happened was that Mal, Phil and I gathered around a microphone and blew the drones—the big pipes sticking out the top of a bagpipe—and then that was 'looped' by George. That basically meant that we played the drones for a few seconds and George made a tape loop to repeat those few seconds over and over, to give the impression of a continuous drone, essential to the sound of the pipes. The tape was also slowed at the start to give that peculiar drag the pipes have when they kick in. Those pipes created a shitload of extra work for George on top of the job of editing the original take. Some piece of work, eh?

But 'It's a Long Way to the Top' didn't last too long in our live set. A problem with performing the song live was the bloody bagpipes. We hit on a solution. We took the tape loop of the bagpipe drone that was used on the record, put that onto a cassette, and blasted it through the PA while Bon blew on the chanter—that's the recorder-like bit of the pipes—and hit an approximation of the notes over the taped drone. Not ideal, but sort of workable. A painful part of the deal was that we had to tune up to the drone before the show, or it would be horrendous. Ralph the Roadie would bring the cassette deck backstage and put it through an amp for us to tune to, then whip back out the front with the cassette deck for the house mixer. That's how we battled through with the song, up until we did a show in 1975 at the Hordern Pavilion in Sydney with one of our archrivals, hit-makers Skyhooks.

Now, we always wanted to blow away any band we supported, but it went double, maybe even triple for Skyhooks. They were enjoying considerably more success than us at that point; their album *Living in the Seventies* was everywhere. We felt it was our duty to correct this. I don't know if it was arrogance but we believed that we could out-rock every band in Australia—and that showed in our general attitude. There were some bands around—or should I say, most bands—that we held in contempt, often with some justification. This was an ongoing thing in my time with the guys; there was always some band that was perceived to be doing better than us and they would be our next target. We'd take their success personally. It wasn't the most endearing trait, but it motivated us enormously. It was the ultimate in 'us versus them'—it was us versus *all* of them, Skyhooks especially.

What we needed with the Skyhooks show wasn't just a great gig, but a big finish. Something that would send the kids home talking about us, not Skyhooks. Michael Browning came up with the idea that we should create a commotion on stage at the end of the show and that a couple of big guys—Michael being one of them—would rush onto the stage, dressed as uniformed cops, and nick us. Well, that was the plan anyway. The idea had its genesis in a shoot with the photographer Philip Morris, which took place at Lavender Bay, on the beautiful Sydney Harbour, near Luna Park. Michael and a pal were dressed as policemen and were in the act of apprehending the band, presumably for some misdemeanour, while Philip snapped away. So it was agreed that Michael and his pal would don the police uniforms again for the climax of the Hordern show.

The set proceeded well, and the band went over as we'd hoped. As we finished 'Baby Please Don't Go', Bon was right up on the edge of the stage, leaning over and winding up the first few rows. It was typical Bon stuff, leering into the crowd, sussing out the good-looking girls. As he was doing this, I walked up behind Bon and gave him a tap on the arse with my foot. It didn't seem like much but it was enough to send him sprawling into the front rows, and Bon disappeared under a tidal wave of arms and legs.

Still, there wasn't the desired commotion on stage, so I tackled Angus and had a general roll around with him. It was nothing too heated, just a little friendly wrestle, but it was enough to send the road crew into a spin; they were scurrying around trying to protect the microphones and stands that were getting knocked about. This was where things got a bit out of hand. While our crew was fine, nobody else knew of our planned prank, and we'd damaged some mics and monitor boxes, and the PA guys had the shits. So there was plenty of to and fro, and certainly no shortage of profanity, threats, and push and shove. We were escorted off the stage by Browning and a pal of his, our mission accomplished, and the search party finally returned with Bon, who'd had the wind completely knocked out of him. He was out cold.

Backstage, Bon was propped up, breathing into a brown paper bag. One of the first people into our dressing room was Margaret Young, Mal and Angus's sister, the maker of fine velvet school uniforms to the stars, who wasn't in on what had just occurred on stage. Margaret was the only daughter of the Young clan of Burwood and followed closely in the family mould—she was small of stature, fiercely loyal and not backward in coming forward.

She came straight at me and said, 'Leave my little brother alone.' She said it with a smile but I certainly felt there was an edge there. She wasn't one to trifle with, Margaret, so I got the message. She was quick off the mark; I'll give her that.

Angus was relatively cool, although a tad ruffled by the impromptu wrestling match, but he got that it was all part of the 'plan'. Margaret definitely wasn't convinced and I was getting one of those looks that may have been reserved for misbehaving little brothers.

For the next ten minutes or so, we all shared a few beers—except for Angus, of course, who sipped away at his chocolate milk—and had a few laughs about what had just happened, while keeping a watchful eye on the recuperating Mr Scott, who still had his loaf in the brown paper bag. Outside there was a nasty-sounding commotion brewing. There was banging on the door, threats of violence and the sounds of gear and people getting thrown around. Finally our door burst open and in rolled a rather rotund roadie from the PA crew, absolutely steaming. What didn't help was a quip from somebody—I suspect Phil, who was always one for a quick, smartarse comment, particularly if someone was being a big pain in the arse.

'Quick, hide the sandwiches.'

Well, that was it, the already angry roadie exploded. Ranting about how we had no respect—true—couldn't care less about the next act—yep, true again—and we were never going to use their PA again—another tick, and so what? He then pulled our bagpipe cassette out of his pocket and threw it against the wall, smashing the thing to bits. He rolled back out of the room, leaving all of us in stunned silence.

Bon took his head out of his brown paper bag and ran a bloodshot eye over what had just gone down. Then he broke the uneasy silence.

'That fat fucker killed our pipes.'

Billy Thorpe once wrote something insightful about AC/DC. He noted that Johnny O'Keefe, Australia's first home-grown rock superstar, saw Billy coming—and Billy said he saw AC/DC coming. And I believe you can draw a direct line from the Aztecs, Billy's band, to AC/DC—it's also well worth noting that Michael Browning managed both acts. They were part of the same kick-arse pub rock culture that shaped many Australian bands; Rose Tattoo, Midnight Oil and INXS among them. There was a common attitude, basically: 'If you don't like it, too bad, fuck off.'

My pals and I used to check out bands at the Hard Rock before I joined AC/DC, and I can remember seeing Browning at the ticket box taking the door money. I wondered why the cover charge was $2.10—it was always $2.10 to get in. It was a weird amount. When I started working with Michael and AC/DC, I asked him about it.

'It's so the mugs put their change in the pinball machines.'

Now, is that a manager or what? If you are doing business, you want a guy like that on your side of the table—or the pinball machine.

I saw a load of great bands at the Hard Rock Café. It was rough as hell but had a great vibe. I imagined it was how the Cavern in Liverpool once was; we later learned that the Marquee in London was very similar. The club was hot, sweaty, just ready-made for rock and roll. The bands would play in the basement area; you'd have to walk through the crowd to get to the stage. There was no division between band and punters.

When AC/DC started to pull big crowds to the Hard Rock—I played my first gig there with the band in May 1975, and we played there at least seven times in that month alone—we had to use Michael's office upstairs as a dressing room. You couldn't get through the crowd downstairs. We'd get ready, walk out the front door and around into Flinders Street while Ralph the Roadie was unscrewing one of the big industrial fans at the back of the stage. Then we'd climb in through the hole, straight onto the stage. Ralph would seal us in and that would then become our escape route after the show. As the set ended, Ralph would be waiting out on the street, screwdriver in hand. (My future in-laws actually owned the building that housed the Hard Rock—strange but true. I'm sure if they were my in-laws while I was in the band Michael would have hoped for a better deal on the rent.)

The Hard Rock might have been the band's HQ, but the suburban beer barns formed the AC/DC heartland. You could land yourself in a bit of bother in the pubs, even if you were on stage, as we found out. Over a few months in mid-1975 things got a bit dicey for us. We had developed a reputation as bad boys—or at least, that was the image that was projected—and it seemed that an 'unruly element' (I read a newspaper article that described our following with those very words) was attracted to the band. In fact, if you had a good look around at those pub gigs, 'unruly element' described the majority of the crowd pretty well. Mix it together with loud rock and roll and plenty of beer and things could get interesting.

It all exploded on the one and only night we played the Manhattan Hotel at Ringwood, an outer suburban venue, also in May '75. The Manhattan Hotel was a typical beer barn, a fairly new hotel/motel complex, with function rooms for weddings, twenty-firsts and the like, and it featured a large, open auditorium for live entertainment—with ample fighting room. There was also a mezzanine level, a balcony-style arrangement that was usually kept closed, although it was open when we played there because of the extra punters. The venue was crowded, loud and smoky—and the natives were restless that night.

The chaos began well before we started our set. We were in the dressing room, out the back of the stage, during the support band's set, and all we could hear was the sound of tables and chairs being overturned and glasses getting smashed. We were already feeling a bit anxious when Ralph the Roadie gave us a report.

'You are all out of your minds if you go out there,' he chuckled, looking back over his shoulder.

Cheers, Ralph.

Gig time was now upon us, so out we went anyway, to a

mighty roar. Even though I felt a bit like a Christian entering the Colosseum, my initial thought was, 'Well, this isn't so bad, we'll get away with this.' But with each skirmish that broke out, there was a more spirited response from the bouncers, and that sparked off a shower of beer glasses. It was getting 'tropical', as they say in Melbourne when trouble is brewing. It was especially nasty when the glasses started raining down from the mezzanine level; people were now getting cut up, as well as being thumped.

The violence ebbed and flowed—there'd be an ugly peak then things would calm down for five or ten minutes before breaking out again. Angus didn't help things by climbing up on the PA and providing an irresistible target for the glass-chuckers. He was summarily pelted. The first volley of glasses all missed him, but before he could climb down a glass hit his guitar neck, near his left hand. He was lucky not to get messed up a lot worse than he did. There was a bit of blood, but nothing too nasty. More than anything, it scared the crap out of him, and I couldn't blame Angus for feeling that way, either. I was glad I wasn't in the firing line, three metres up in the air.

I think Angus handled it very well, but he was mighty pissed off, let me tell you. Angus may have been tiny but he had a sizeable temper; it was a beauty, he could really blast off. If he'd been a big bloke I'm sure he really would have caused some serious damage. So that was it for us; we were off. We bolted for the sanctuary (or so we hoped) of the dressing room, with three of the largest bouncers guarding our way. It was the only way in or out, I noticed. We'd never bailed mid-gig before, but we had no intention of becoming moving targets for a bunch of glass-throwing meatheads.

We could hear it was getting more than a tad tropical out front when Ralph made it back to the dressing room. He was as white as a sheet.

'What happened?' someone asked. Ralph said he'd just seen a bloke get thrown off the balcony and make a three-point landing on some fellow punters below. It wasn't long before the sirens of police cars and ambulances cut through the noise. Thankfully, things started to calm down. The place was cleared out and shut down, but we were advised to sit still until we got the all-clear. We settled in with some beers and counted ourselves a very lucky rock band. It could have been very, very messy.

We left the hotel the best part of an hour later, while there were still three ambulances and a strong police presence cleaning up the mess. I was happy to be part of a very loud, smartarse rock band but I didn't sign up to get pelted with beer glasses. That was the only time I felt we might have been in a situation that we couldn't handle.

It was in August 1975 when all hell broke loose again, this time at the Matthew Flinders Hotel, a venue on the east side of Melbourne. It was another big place, a real beer barn that held around 1200 people. The place was full. We plugged in at 10 pm and were to play two sets, finishing a little before closing time at midnight. The gig was going along at the normal clip, when Angus launched into his usual number, going offstage into the crowd during 'Baby Please Don't Go'. He'd spin around on his back on the dance floor, kicking his legs up and rolling around, playing all the while, while the band chugged along back on the stage. Pat Pickett, who was also one of our roadies, would run Angus's guitar lead out to him, so you could always spot him—usually there'd be a circle of interested onlookers gathered around watching Angus play.

I didn't see what started things off this night but some agitation caught my eye through the crowd, five metres or so from the stage, while Angus was doing his thing. The next thing I know Phil took off into the crowd, jumping straight over the top of his drums. Phil wasn't a naturally aggro person, but there wasn't an ounce of fear in the guy, as far as I could tell. Phil had grown up on the north side of Melbourne, in Rosanna, and judging by some of his mates who turned up at the early gigs they sure looked like guys you'd prefer to have inside the tent pissing out. One of his mates was known as 'the Indian'; he was a swarthy-looking guy, real quiet, with a handgun permanently tucked down the back of his high-waisted jeans. A serious character.

Anyway, what Phil had seen was some guys kicking the crap out of our schoolboy guitarist. I dropped my bass and took off after Phil. Mal was still firmly planted on the stage, Bon was, I think, in the dressing room at the time. For maybe the first and only time, AC/DC was a one-man band. As Phil reached Angus he smashed one guy with a mighty crack; I heard it clearly over Malcolm's guitar. Pat was doing his usual fine job of protecting 'Little Albie', as Angus was called, and was handing out some summary justice, as was Phil. I was also helping out but they had it well covered. Angus had taken a few on board but there was no real damage done.

It was just settling down—Malcolm was still playing!—when I saw a guy make a move towards Phil. I got him just in time, but one of the bouncers, a massive, bearded guy called Ivan, didn't recognise me as one of the band and hit me with a huge clenched-fist backhander. I went straight down on my arse, skidding backwards. It would have been funny if it wasn't me. It was a very solid hit, right on the nose. I could taste blood straight away, and the sound of the hit was nasty, too—percussive, a real brain rattler. Not a sharp one because of the size of Ivan's fist, just a real big thud.

Eventually we stumbled back on stage to finish 'Baby Please Don't Go'. I was doing a piss-poor impersonation of Kiss's Gene Simmons, spitting some blood, but no big deal, I'd lived through worse. What was a big deal was the crack I heard when Phil smacked one of Angus's assailants. It wasn't the guy's nose that made the noise, as I'd thought; it was Phil's thumb, which he'd broken.

After an unscheduled trip to the Alfred Hospital to get Phil's thumb seen to, we had two gigs the next day, which was a Friday. We had a shopping-mall appearance for a few songs then a pub show later on. Phil managed the shopping-mall gig playing with one hand, but we had to blow out the pub gig. We were off to Western Australia the following week, but Phil, whose hand was swollen and painful, clearly wasn't a starter.

ϟ

As Mal proved that night at the Matthew Flinders, playing while all hell was breaking loose on the dance floor, the show must go on. So Colin Burgess, AC/DC's drummer from the very early days, was called in to cover for Phil. The plan was for Phil to travel with the band and get up and do a couple of tunes each night, playing one-handed. And Phil did have some form as a one-armed drummer. When he was a little bloke, he'd entered a talent quest, playing drums with one stick—don't know what he was doing with the other one. He ripped into Sandy Nelson's opus 'Let There Be Drums' and won the contest. Phil maintained that he was hooked on drumming from that moment.

But like most best-laid plans, it came unstuck. When we got to Perth in late September '75, Phil was still having some real trouble with his thumb and got it checked out again at a hospital, and was dead lucky that he did. The damage was more serious than we originally thought; if he'd followed the advice he got in Melbourne there was a chance he might have lost some use of his thumb. Not an ideal situation for a drummer.

So with Phil undergoing an operation, we continued with Colin Burgess, playing gigs in Geraldton, Katanning, Bunbury, Kalgoorlie and Perth. Bon shared a room with Colin; they were acquaintances from the sixties when Bon was in the Valentines and Colin was playing in the Master's Apprentices, a highly rated Aussie band. And those two 'old blokes' got up to some serious shenanigans, which I witnessed, although their choice of female company seemed to the rest of us to be well past it. I invaded the old blokes' room at the White Sands Hotel with Pat Pickett. One of their boilers had passed out naked on a bed in a rather unflattering position.

'Shit, it looks like she's pinched Roy Rogers' saddlebags,' said Pat.

Now, I'm sure Pat wouldn't have minded me telling you that he was no Brad Pitt even back then. So if Pat turned up his nose at a prospective 'research assistant', well, they had to be pretty crook.

I think it was a very welcome break for Bon to have someone on the road with him that he could relate to—even in their choice of female partners. Bon could suffer on the road; some days he'd seem lonely and depressed. He couldn't—wouldn't—try to hide it, either; that just wasn't in his make-up. Bon always wore his heart on his sleeve. Colin provided the kind of camaraderie that was quite possibly missing with the rest of us, maybe because of the age difference—Bon was from a different generation, after all. In a sad footnote, Bon was drinking with Colin at the Music Machine in London on the last night of his life.

I did learn something during Phil's absence from the band, which must have been very plain to all concerned. While Colin did a serviceable job filling in, not having Phil there left a gaping hole in the band's sound. I couldn't believe it. I was quite prepared to cope with some difference but I genuinely felt that the arse dropped out of the band without Phil. It's not that Colin wasn't up to it—not so—but Phil was (and still is) an indispensable part of the AC/DC sound.

It was an awkward couple of weeks playing with Colin. There was no option other than to battle on, but it felt like the band was limping rather than galloping. The guitars were still firing, Bon and Angus were up to their normal stunts out front, but the feel was lost; it was a different band altogether. We still went over reasonably well but it was light years away from what it should have been. It was a relief to get Phil back in the ranks.

Chapter 5

'If this lasts past the first song, it's a fucking miracle'

Life in AC/DC was dictated by a weekly work sheet. The work sheet that we received was low on info, but it had all the pertinent guff. It basically set out all our gigs for the week, start times, where the fuck it was and if it was out of town whether we came back after the show or not. The system worked well; the only time it misfired was when Bon failed to read the fine print.

We had a lunchtime gig at the Hard Rock Café (a school-holiday job), starting at 1 pm. No worries—that is, if you followed the work sheet closely enough. Come one o'clock and we were there, all ready to go, with the exception of Bon. By 1.30 pm, still no Bon. Thus began one of the more unusual AC/DC shows, if not the most unusual—a four-piece AC/DC with Mal and Angus on lead vocals. The guys had a real dip at it and it had its moments, but we got the gig done in record time, maybe thirty minutes tops. Fortunately, the Hard Rock was jammed with AC/DC schoolies of the most rabid type, who took to the band even without Bon. I think they were satisfied to have a good scream and passed the Bon-less time trying to drag one of us off the tiny Hard Rock stage. It was good sport all round.

Had it been any other gig we wouldn't have been paid, but on this one we lucked out; after all, it was our manager's club. Our intrepid Mr Scott was finally located later that day. He was a little the worse for wear and tear but was getting back into shape for the gig at the Hard Rock that he believed was to kick off at 1 am. Not even close.

That work sheet ruled my world; I went where the band decreed. I got the feeling that the only acceptable excuse for a 'no show' was that the doctors wouldn't let you out of the hospital, and even then it would be frowned upon. And Browning would probably ask for a doctor's certificate, and then work out some promotional 'angle' to milk the moment. I did sense a loss of freedom to do as I pleased (like go see Carlton belt Collingwood), but the upside was this crowd followed us around. The band was the social scene for loads of mates, new and old, so it was pretty much a party on wheels. If my pals turned up at a gig, they were up for a big night, so it was a case of 'Gentlemen, start your engines', find some girls to crank it up or some other substance to do the trick.

Quickly, AC/DC came to dominate my whole being; it became my life. We were together because we were a band but AC/DC was an entity on its own that commanded all my time and attention. I had no option but to follow it with blind faith. It became my career, livelihood, social life and, hopefully, my future. The cliché would be 'It was my family', but it was never that, it was something else again. If you were in AC/DC you lived it, it wasn't an act. I wasn't just one part of a band; I became part of a lifestyle. It was the reason we were all together; the only way it made sense was that we were only AC/DC when we were together in the same room.

I was still living at the Hilton; I wouldn't stay with the band when in Melbourne. I'd get dropped off at the Hilton after a show if nothing else was on but I would be back with the guys at the Freeway Gardens (the band's new abode in Melbourne, having outgrown our old HQ) by early afternoon the next day. That's the way it was; I felt compelled to be there. I had my home at the Hilton and I'm sure Phil thought of his mum's place as home, as did Mal and Angus with the family home in Sydney. Essentially, however, we were all homeless; all I owned was my equipment and my clothes. It was a real gypsy lifestyle.

Glynis, my former girlfriend, had drifted into the social circle of the band. Although we were no longer a couple, we were still very close as buddies. It could be a little awkward if one of us was getting some potentially amorous attention. But we did a lot of growing up together. There were tough times, especially the night the band dropped me off at her home in Dandenong, very late one night after a show. I was sent in with condolences from everyone in the band. Her brother Alun had drowned while swimming at an English beach. It was one of the toughest things I'd ever had to do.

ϟ

We mightn't have sounded or looked much like the Bay City Rollers or Sherbet, but that doesn't mean that AC/DC didn't appeal to the kids. At the height of the teenybopper era, when the Rollers and David Cassidy and Donny Osmond ruled the airwaves and the charts, we were booked to play at Melbourne's leading department store, the Myer Emporium, during late August 1975, the school holidays, probably on the strength of our *Countdown* appearances. The plan was for us to play at lunchtime in the 'Miss Melbourne' shop, which was on the first floor of the Bourke Street building. What impressed me was the deal: it was four lunchtime sets, Monday through Thursday, and we were going to pick up $2000 for our trouble. It was real good chaff for doing daytime shows in the city with the night free for more gigs and dollars.

So we headed into the city late on a Monday morning for the first of our four dates with the young girls. Before I joined the band, getting into the city was a very simple matter of walking out of the Hilton and onto Malvern Road and hopping on the number 72 tram for the ten-minute ride into town. It was a different deal now I was in AC/DC.

Michael Browning laid down a few rules that were to be adhered to at all times, and one of them related to public transport. Michael had been riding on a tram when he spotted the duo Bobby & Laurie, real pop stars back in the late 1960s, in the same carriage. It disappointed Michael—his vision of pop stardom took in limousines, not trams. So no band of his would catch public transport, thanks very much. Another of Michael's steadfast rules was that there would be no watches worn on stage. 'Why should you need watches?' he figured. We were rock-and-rollers—surely time was irrelevant to us when we were playing. Where else could we possibly need to be? While I don't mind jumping on a Melbourne tram these days, the watch rule has stuck with me and I dutifully get rid of my timepiece before every show. If

I see someone with a watch on stage, it gets me wondering: 'Have to be somewhere else, do we?' They're supposed to be steaming into it, entertaining, not sneaking in a quick look at how much longer they have to play.

Anyway, there we were, with a run of dates on the female-fashion level of a Melbourne department store. We came prepared—we'd hired an extra PA, lights and a complete replacement back line of amps and drums. Logistically speaking it was impossible to use our normal gear; it would have killed our crew, if they hadn't already killed us for making them load in and out of a city department store each day to make a gig that night. We were to play on a makeshift stage, and on that Monday, a little after midday, we stood there watching the crowd build and build. It was getting pretty tight in the Miss Melbourne shop, when Michael came over to us, rubbed his hands together and said: 'If this lasts past the first song, it's a fucking miracle.' There had to be a couple of thousand kids squeezed into the place.

Our exposure on *Countdown* definitely brought on board a totally new audience, which put us in this weird position where we were liked by both boofheads and screaming teens. Maybe it was Angus's virginal schoolboy legs that did the trick—who can tell? I never saw us as a 'pop' band; seriously, how could you? Once you saw the band live, you got it. Whether you wanted it was another thing, but that was an AC/DC strong point: you dug us or despised us. Mal figured it was preferable to get booed off than to be viewed with indifference. 'At least they'd remember you,' he'd say, and rightly so. The gigs we played divided us from the pop bands, too. I don't think Sherbet would have got out alive from some of the joints we played in.

We didn't have a lot of time to think about our new audience or Michael's comment that day at the Miss Melbourne Shop, however, because it was show time. On we went, no announcement, no fuss, let's get stuck in. We all got onto the stage from Mal's side. Yet even as Bon approached his microphone, girls were trying to drag him offstage. Angus and I got around behind him and plugged in. The noise was unbelievable, but from the crowd, not from us. You would have thought it was the Beatles playing, not a bunch of unkempt, snotty, pimply rockers. I had never heard screaming like that. It was this constant roar that seemed to be coming from all directions at once.

For the life of me, I can't recall what song we tried to start with. We'd only made it through the first couple of bars when the stage was charged by waves of keening banshees. And I mean *waves*. I was a few metres back from the front of the stage, and thankfully so, because I saw Bon disappear completely under a rolling scrum of teenage girls—and there were more coming over the top, and *fast*. It was like Custer's Last Stand, the Indians just kept on coming, all played out in the Myer Miss Melbourne shop. Phil's drums were getting trashed, the back line on my side toppled over and I scrambled over the top of that, out the back through the change rooms and into a storage area and some sanctuary, or so I thought. The screams then got louder and closer. I had no idea where the other guys were. It was pandemonium, like a scene straight out of *A Hard Day's Night*.

Bon was chased through the building by screaming teens, with his loyal sidekick, Pat Pickett, right behind him. They ended up going out the other side of the building into Elizabeth Street and making their escape back to our base at the

Freeway Gardens Hotel by tram, ironically enough. (Thereby breaking a Browning Rule of the Road, but there were mitigating circumstances.) I sat in the storage area for a good twenty minutes with what sounded like the D-Day landing at Normandy going on out in the store.

We had set off a full-on, screaming, knicker-wetting teenage riot. But what blew the whole thing way out of hand was that it provided some of our fans with an excellent chance to snag a few free samples of Miss Melbourne gear. The place got cleaned out.

When things simmered down a little, I walked out, still in my stage clothes and carrying my bass, went down the escalator on to Bourke Street. I jumped straight into a cab back to the Prahran Hilton. I had to borrow a fiver from Uncle Morry, who ran the deli on the ground floor of the Hilton, so I could pay the cab fare. Morry was a survivor from Dachau, with an unbelievably great sense of humour for someone who lived through the horrors of a Nazi concentration camp. When I walked in with my bass still around my neck, a bit the worse for wear, Morry looked at me, his shoulders raised and arms wide apart, palms up.

'You don't have a case for that thing, big shot?'

Chapter 6

'I know she's here with one of those little pricks'

AC/DC was a band that seemed to survive on momentum: as long as we were moving forward, there were no problems. Now that we'd had some success in Australia, our next move was obvious. In the 1970s, Australian acts with any aspirations were drawn to England; it was the accepted rite of passage. And it didn't just apply to rock and roll bands—it was the logical next step for actors, directors, writers and pretty much anyone involved with the arts. Expat Aussies such as Clive James, Brett Whiteley, Richard Neville, Barry Humphries and Germaine Greer had made the leap, while the Easybeats and Bon's old band Fraternity had tried their luck in 'Mother England', along with loads of other Aussie groups. The Master's Apprentices had even recorded at Abbey Road studios, a sacred site for the Beatles. In the ensuing years England was the destination for Nick Cave, the Triffids, the Saints and the Go-Betweens.

Billy Thorpe and the Aztecs had toured the UK, but without much luck. When Michael Browning was Billy's manager, he and his sister Coral, who was UK-based, were instrumental in talking the Aztecs up in London and getting some dates at the prestigious music industry showcase, the Speakeasy.

The Speakeasy, while a very cool and groovy place to hang out (and to pick up good-looking women, as I would learn) was the size of a shoebox. The idea of the Aztecs in there at full throttle was terrifying; it would have been unbearable. The joint relied on conversation to do deals—business, drug-related or sexual—so the Aztecs would have stopped the place from functioning. That was in the days of Barry McKenzie, too, when Australians were stereotyped as buffoons. The Aztecs were probably thought of as such, albeit horrendously loud buffoons. The Aztecs proceeded to blast the place to smithereens; they lasted one set and got shown the door, quick smart.

The reality was that AC/DC was a band that could deliver, night after night, in the studio, on the road, wherever. Had AC/DC not been up to it, they would have ended up like so many Australian acts of the time: a hit here, a tour there and endless *Countdown* appearances, only to fizzle out or disappear into the club scene, eventually banding together with other also-rans in a retro/revival/nursing-home tour. A major factor in AC/DC's favour was aggressive, go-for-it representation. Other bands had strong management, such as Sherbet, who worked with Roger Davies. But even though they had a hit in the UK with 'Howzat', Roger just couldn't crack it for them outside of Oz. (Roger later would relaunch Tina Turner's career and handle Janet Jackson and Pink, so he did more than okay in the end.)

Sherbet's 'Howzat' was a source of aggravation for a few of us in AC/DC: we were out there on the road building a following and these guys walked straight into a hit record, or so it seemed to us. We'd rarely admit to our frustration, though. That's just the way we worked: we judged our progress in relation to other bands, those we felt we were competing against. In Australia it was Sherbet and Skyhooks—they were the big acts and our targets. We had absolutely no regard for either of those bands, so what was the big deal about overtaking them in Australia? Who the fuck cared? Their appeal was completely lost on us, so we figured, why not go play with the big boys instead? It was obvious that heading overseas was the only way for us to keep moving and growing.

Michael Browning had been targeting England for us for quite some time—in fact, I believe that the band agreed to hire him as a manager because of his desire to take them 'offshore'. Michael's ambition would have certainly rung true with Alberts, and George Young, in particular. It's likely that George, AC/DC's mentor, who'd come so close to breaking in the UK with the Easybeats, was dreaming of another shot. And the band was just as hungry as George.

From the very first day I met the guys, the UK was the target. It was almost preordained. I initially took the plans for the UK with more than a grain of salt but it didn't take long for me to realise that there was never any doubt; it was *definitely* going to happen. It would have been blasphemy to suggest otherwise. I'm sure if I had voiced any doubts it would have been seen as mutiny. I would have been made to walk the plank, for sure. It was a no-brainer anyway. We had built up a full head of steam in Australia very quickly, had two very successful albums and some hits, so where could we go from there? We had to get the band overseas.

Michael had flown to London in mid-1975 to sound out interest. He worked his way around London carrying what we called his 'Maxwell Smart' briefcase video player, a pretty sophisticated device. It was the stuff of MI5 and secret agents. Michael quickly became known as 'that Aussie bloke with the briefcase'. He played all and sundry the video for 'High Voltage', from a Festival Hall show with Skyhooks. In the clip, in the midst of the crowd shots, there are a few white banners supported by poles, held in the air by fans, emblazoned with AC/DC. Among these is my particular favourite, a big banner that read: ANGUS U SPUNK. All the handiwork on that was courtesy of one Angus Young. He had spent the previous afternoon on the lounge room floor of Chateau AC/DC creating his masterpiece. The suits in London weren't to know; they just saw a crowd going nuts.

Michael's sister Coral opened some doors for us, which helped no end. Coral, who'd been in London for five years, had worked for A&M Records and had been involved with the Rolling Stones. Coral was very well connected and well liked; she was a very positive, upbeat person who was working every contact she had to get things happening for AC/DC. She would become our go-between—she knew all the people, all the clubs, and she understood how the music scene worked. She was our mum away from home and Coral, who'll excuse me for saying this, was also very easy on the eyes. Coral has that great quality of many Aussie girls—they can be smokin' hot, terrific for your self-esteem *and* also be really good, close pals.

The aim of Michael's first trip was to secure the band a record deal and get the *High Voltage* LP a release. If he failed, the fallback plan was to organise some showcase gigs in

London in October/November 1975, ideally at the Marquee and the Speakeasy, two inner-city London gigs that were frequented by the taste-makers that might get a vibe happening for us. Michael met with Phil Carson and Dave Dee at Atlantic Records and thankfully a deal was struck. Atlantic was the label of choice for Led Zeppelin and Bad Company, among many others. We were on our way, even if it was a little later than the band had planned. By ten days, actually.

Before we shipped out for the Old Dart, Michael seized the opportunity to get us into the studio in January 1976 to record the follow up to TNT, which was still selling well at home. In fact, the ongoing success of TNT would eventually delay the Australian release of its successor, Dirty Deeds Done Dirt Cheap. Recording Dirty Deeds followed the now familiar AC/DC studio routine—cook up a few riffs and bits at soundchecks and before gigs, then wedge two weeks of studio time with George and Harry into our virtually non-stop touring schedule. We were planning our exodus to the UK so who was to know when we would be able to get back inside a studio?

We'd made a quick pit stop at Alberts prior to the Dirty Deeds sessions to record 'Jailbreak' and 'Fling Thing', so we had a little head start on the album. But it was to be the typical 'hothouse' approach: working up the tunes with George and getting the backing tracks down in the first week, leaving the second week for guitar solos and vocals.

George, Mal and Angus were settled in, running through the ideas at the piano, putting the riffs through the wringer, before we got down to the business of nailing a backing track. This was George at his best, in his element, being AC/DC's cheerleader/mentor, driving the band and pointing us in the right direction in the studio.

The tracks started to mount up. 'Ain't No Fun Waitin' Round to Be a Millionaire' was one that got me; it still does, it's a cracker. The way it kicks in again for the outro—brilliant. Mal used Ike and Tina Turner's version of 'Proud Mary' as a signpost. We stuck with the by-now standard process of locking Bon away in the kitchen and keeping him hostage until he delivered more of his 'dirty ditties' and 'Ain't No Fun' was Bon at his most laconic, while 'Ride On' was, I reckon, at least semi-autobiographical. It's Bon through and through, singing a super, straight out blues.

One time, when we hit a wall and the ideas dried up, George got into the amp room, picked up my Gibson Ripper bass and started playing a shuffle. He'd lit the fuse, getting the guys to swing into what would become 'There's Gonna Be Some Rockin''. That was typical George, leading the charge. I've always thought it must have been such a buzz for Malcolm and Angus to work so closely with George, three brothers united—well, sort of. I'd be lying if I said I wasn't envious of their relationship, no matter how volatile it could be at times.

'Problem Child' was another killer track, yet it was one of only three Dirty Deeds tunes that made the live set list during my tenure with the band (the others were 'Dirty Deeds' and 'Jailbreak'). It was strange—there were some great Dirty Deeds tracks that never saw any degree of roadwork at all. 'Ride On' would have killed it live with Angus wailing, building a searing solo, but it simply didn't find a place in the thirty-minute support sets that were to become our standard in the UK and Europe.

Travelling overseas was a long-held dream for me and here I was, about to do it in a band that we all believed was going to brain it. I was definitely under the impression that we were all in it for the long haul; that went without saying. Then again, looking back, maybe I should have cleared that one up with the guys. Oops. My take on our overseas relocation was simple: it was an adventure. I was looking forward to London in particular and I'm sure Malcolm, Angus and Bon were extra keen to get back to Scotland, given their roots. But it wasn't seen as cool in AC/DC if you got too excited about anything, so I learned to take it all in my stride. This was simply the next step forward for us all, even though on the inside I was seriously pumped.

We had no idea what to expect, although we knew we were starting at the bottom again. But that held no fears for us; it's my feeling we functioned best as underdogs. And what a way to see the UK and Europe, playing in a band that was red hot. That may sound as smug as fuck but that's the way it felt; I was confident we could play on any bill and do the business. We were arrogant little pricks on more than a few occasions—and so what? All it needed was for enough people to be exposed to the band live and for us to do the right shows, then we could let the music-biz machinery do its job. This trip was the start of the next important phase for AC/DC. It held some interesting twists and turns for me, too.

My family was excited for me. There was no big send-off but we had a nice little get-together at home, a lamb roast and a few drinks. But that was no big deal, just family business as usual. That's the way it was. There was no huge fanfare in the press either, pretty much in line with the band's 'no bullshit' stance. AC/DC always went about its business in an understated manner: get in there, get the job done and hit it very hard. Take no prisoners.

My close buddies were suitably impressed, but some of their noses were a little out of joint—their free passport into gigs and clubs, namely me, was pissing off to London. Of course, entree into gigs wasn't the main issue here; their love lives had improved considerably by hanging out with a happening band. Now they had to do their own scoring.

It was a good thing that I was leaving the country, actually. I'd been avoiding a very large and extremely irate husband, who'd been prowling the lobby of our hotel the night before our departure, yelling: 'I know she's here with one of those little pricks.' (He was right, by the way.) I was a quick learner and had found out that it was always best to tip your hotel's concierge well, as he/she would then be honour-bound to pass on any vital information that concerned you and your wellbeing. Still, I couldn't escape Oz quickly enough.

The minor media send-off at Sydney Airport was also covered by our associates at *Countdown*. Mal and Phil spoke a little bit, but looked pretty damned uncomfortable—even Bon was a tad apprehensive as we were quizzed about our 'escape' from Australia. I kept my trap shut. I'd been up all night, taking care of some important last-minute business.

By the time the cameras were rolling late morning I was feeling no pain. In the footage I've since seen of the press conference I'm doing a very passable impersonation of a deaf mute. One of the band's few close friends, Ted Mulry, was there leading the cheer squad and when a *Countdown* promo was shot with Bon and Angus, I snuck in behind him and lifted Ted up onto my shoulders. I have no idea where my super strength came from, especially after the night I'd just had.

We landed at London's Heathrow Airport on 1 April 1976, April Fool's Day. It was an extremely long flight, with stops in Singapore, Hong Kong, Bombay (now Mumbai) and Bahrain and then, finally, London. I was in transit for thirty-six hours and forty-five minutes. We flew Garuda, in a Boeing 707, so it was like spending a day and a half on a cattle truck. I had time for two hangovers on the way.

As we drew closer to Heathrow, I was keen to sight any remote piece of England at all, but was thwarted by what I discovered to be regulation English cloud cover. We were descending when the thick cover parted just enough to frame the Tower Bridge and the River Thames for a moment or two. It was exhilarating for me, surreal, just like a movie. Was that stuff really down there? I gave Phil a nudge but before he could get a look, the clouds had swallowed the Tower Bridge. But Phil's quick reaction showed that he was just as keen as me to take it all in.

During the flight we were impatient; we just wanted to get there and get working. That was the band in those days: it was about work, work and work, and if we weren't working, we were waiting to work, wanting to work. That was especially true for Angus. While Mal was the captain of the ship, calling the shots, Angus lived and breathed for the band and for his Gibson SG guitar. Angus's essentials were pretty simple: his Gibson and AC/DC (they were inseparable), Benson & Hedges ciggies, cups of tea, chocolate and spaghetti bolognese—but NO parmesan cheese, or there would be consequences. Angus and his SG were one; he'd practise by himself for hours each day, no amp, just sitting on his bed, noodling away, his foot stomping all the time, keeping time with the world's longest guitar solo. Come to think of it,

I can't recall hearing Angus play anything but lead solos during his bedroom practice sessions. There was no need to, I guess, not with Mal taking care of the rhythm. It wouldn't be unusual for Angus to play for eight hours on a day off. He would have played on the flight to London if he could.

We were very impressed, if you can be impressed after thirty-six hours on a plane, to be met at Heathrow not only by Michael and Coral, but to be poured into a limo supplied by Atlantic Records. We were all a tad gamey after nearly two days in the air, but we did a quick tour of the sights: Buckingham Palace, Trafalgar Square, Nelson's Column, Piccadilly Circus, Big Ben, the Tower of London. All the landmarks I'd seen on TV and in movies (particularly my favourite James Bond movies) were now flashing before my eyes, just as they had briefly during our descent into Heathrow. I found it hard to get my head around the fact that I was actually looking at the real deal and not a Monopoly board. It felt like a small, scaled-down version of the 'real' London—and there were people absolutely everywhere, scurrying about like ants. I felt like jumping out of the limo and getting among it. I really wanted to start exploring. I already had a mental 'to do' list, with the British Museum and its famed Egyptology department at the top.

After the tour we reached our new base at 49 Inverness Terrace, Bayswater. It was a massive terrace house that had been divided into a number of apartments. The band and crew would all live together, which gives some idea about the size of the building: there were seven guys in one apartment. It was the Taj Mahal compared to the band's Lansdowne Road house. As per the standard arrangement, I roomed with Phil. Phil and I shared very similar working-class backgrounds, and both being Melburnians, we were keen followers of VFL. Phil supported Essendon and he'd never hold back when the Bombers beat my team, Carlton. Of course I had the good grace not to harass him when Carlton returned the favour.

Phil and I were pretty much thrown together as roommates, being the new guys on the block. It says something about the pecking order at Inverness Terrace that Bon, Malcolm and Angus each had their own rooms, whereas Phil and I shared a tiny attic room. Phil and I got along well, we were good mates, comfortable with each other from the outset. We shared a lot of laughs. It was Phil who gave me my band nickname, 'Herbie', because I shared a surname with Herbie Evans, a character from the racy Australian TV show *Number 96*.

If I had a problem, Phil was the guy I turned to—and vice versa. We would share confidences that just would not have been possible with Malcolm or Angus. In later times, Phil was the only one with whom I would share any doubts about my longevity with the band. He had doubts about his role, too, and dreamed of opening a restaurant in Melbourne if things came undone.

Our house in Bayswater was five minutes from the Queensway tube station, with the city only a few stops away. You could be slap-bang in the middle of London in ten minutes, or scoot across Hyde Park and onto the King's Road, Chelsea, to do some shopping or hit a few pubs. We were just one street off Queensway, the major shopping precinct of Bayswater.

Soon after arriving, while I was shopping in a Queensway department store, Whiteleys, I was told that Brian Jones of the Rolling Stones had once worked there. This old stuffed shirt in menswear was dismissive of Jones, as if leaving the job was a mistake. 'He wasn't really cut out for the job,' I was told—and what a fucking surprise that was. 'He wasn't really up to it. Nice boy but a pity about the hair.' He then followed with a very sniffy: 'I presume you are in one of those groups, too.' Fuck yeah, pal, and proud of it. It's amazing how people can just tell that you're in a band. I don't think we looked any different from the normal young punters—or at least the punters that came to our gigs—but we would always get the same treatment.

Bayswater was perfect for us. Not just because of its proximity to the city, but there were plenty of takeaway food places and pubs; it had everything we needed. The Ducks and Drakes pub was just around the corner, the ideal place for a lunch of shepherd's pie and a couple of pints, even though the room-temperature beer did take a lot of getting used to. And we had our den mother, Coral Browning, who lived nearby at 33 Ossington Street. I was a major soccer fan and was also very impressed to learn that Jimmy Hill, the compere of the TV soccer show *The Big Match*, lived on the same street as Coral. Now, that was *big* news. I saw Hill on the Queensway on numerous occasions.

ϟ

The aggressive attitude that AC/DC had towards Australian bands continued when we shifted overseas. The world's bigger bands became our new targets. Who the fuck did these pricks think they were? We saw a few of the so-called headline acts and straight away knew that we had nothing to fear.

We weren't seeing or hearing anything that fazed us; more to the point, we were surprised that there was a heap of crap bands around, mainly playing in the clubs and pubs. Most of these fuckers couldn't play—simply getting in tune seemed to be beyond them.

Very early on, we went as a group to see Kiss at the Hammersmith Odeon. We had a ball; it was one of the funniest nights of my life. I mean, really, what the fuck were these guys up to? I know we had a schoolboy playing guitar but what the hell was this? Sure, they'd had a huge run of success but, really, would you want your mates to know that this was what you were up to? As a package it worked a treat; it was clever but contrived and proved to be massively successful over a long period of time. But were Kiss a true rock band? Not in a million years. No wonder they wore make-up.

As soon as the lights dimmed, Kiss started talking it up. 'Good evening, London, we're gonna rock this place to the ground. ROCK AND ROLL, LONDON!' With all due respect to their legions of fans, it was hilarious. Sure, the gig was well staged and brilliantly produced, but it was probably the funniest thing I have ever seen. A cartoon from start to finish. There was an odd thing going on after each song: there seemed to be this massive whoopin' and hollerin' reaction, very American in nature, but I swear most of the punters in the three-quarters-full theatre were trying to work out where all the noise was coming from. It wasn't the British way; that was for sure. Angus was on board for this one, a rare outing for the little bloke. He was just as underwhelmed as the rest of us; the gig wouldn't help entice him out to many more shows, unless he was in need of some light entertainment. This was the opposition?

Believe it or not, one act that we did hold in reasonably high esteem was the Glitter Band. We saw them at Drury Lane, and the band was swinging, really cooking. They had two drummers and a great guitar player wielding a star-shaped axe. They had one hell of a rhythm guitar player setting it all up. And Gary Glitter was a hoot. He looked like a tarted-up wrestler, as if he'd walked straight out of a pantomime. He really laid on the showbiz thick. Like the guys in Kiss, Glitter was funny as hell, but the band could really play. The Glitter Band weren't to be taken seriously, but they were making money and having a ball.

Everything was set up nicely for our first UK tour, opening for Paul Kossoff's Back Street Crawler, who were also with Atlantic Records. We both had records to promote—theirs was called *The Band Plays On*, which proved prophetic—so it was a double bill of convenience for the label. We were starting at the bottom again, opening for someone better known, playing clubs and some unis, but that was okay: to us it was an entree to a new market, a new audience. At least we thought everything was in place, until the wheels started to come off the wagon—or, more precisely, came completely off Paul Kossoff's wagon.

Paul Kossoff was a near-mythical guitar player, who found fame with the British rock band Free. I grew up with Free, loved their stuff, particularly songs like 'All Right Now' and 'The Stealer'—I mean, seriously, don't get me started, I could go on forever. If you were putting a garage band together in the early seventies there was an excellent chance that you were slaughtering at least a few Free songs: I know because I was, pre-AC/DC. I think it's a fair bet the other guys were, too. And although it didn't pay great dividends within AC/DC to show too much excitement towards anything or anyone, I know that Phil was a big fan of Simon Kirke, the drummer in Free and later on Bad Company.

I was really looking forward to meeting Paul Kossoff. I was still buzzing from that Festival Hall gig I'd witnessed a few years ago, when he played with Free. It was a real life-changing night for me. I was now armed with a bunch of questions, handed to me by a young Sydney guitar slinger named Bob Spencer. Bob was an excitable chap, a terrific guitar player and an absolute Kossoff nut; to Bob, Kossoff was more a deity than a mere musician. Bob had slipped me his list of questions when his current band, Finch, was supporting us at a gig in Sydney's northern suburbs. Finch would play their part in my future, too, as it turned out.

Yet even before the tour I'd heard talk from people who knew such things that Kossoff had some serious drug problems, most likely with heroin. We were also told that he'd cleaned up and was getting healthy, or as healthy as he could be while recovering from what must have been an absolute narcotic nightmare. While we were preparing for our trip to London, Kossoff was on his way back from New York, on 19 March 1976. Tragically, he died in his sleep on the plane from heart failure. Another soul lost to the rock and roll lifestyle. Kossoff was twenty-six years old.

It's easy to blame life on the road, the pressures and the temptations that go along with it, for people messing up their lives, becoming arseholes or losing themselves and taking their own life. But I have a theory on this: people who lose their way through drugs, drink or whatever probably would have done it anyway, whether or not they were in a band. There is no doubt that while in a group you can be exposed to a bunch of temptations that you might not encounter in everyday living; that's life on the road. It's ironic, though, that while Kossoff may well have beaten his addiction, the damage he'd already wrought was his undoing.

Paul's father, David Kossoff, a celebrated British actor of the post-war period, made a documentary about his son's downward spiral. The film grew from visits David would make to schools around England to talk about his experience with Paul. The stunning part is where David re-enacts conversations and confrontations they had. David plays himself, and then sits down to play Paul—he sits because Paul wasn't capable of standing, he was that fucked up. It has led me to a belief that drug addicts are basically selfish, so absorbed in their illness they can't see the damage they cause their family and friends, let alone themselves.

The band's reaction to Kossoff's death was fairly offhand; we saw it as a setback for our schedule, pure and simple. We had not one jot of sympathy for Kossoff and grumbled about the inconvenience. We wanted to get out there and rip. Bon summed up our prevailing attitude towards the situation in a missive to *RAM* magazine, back in Australia. 'That cunt Paul Kossoff fucked up our first tour. Wait'll Angus gets hold of him.' We were a sensitive bunch.

So, with Paul Kossoff gone, we had some time on our hands in London. We were not really cut out to be tourists, although I think I spent more time at the British Museum than some of the mummies. As for my roomie Phil, he became a movie cameraman, of sorts. This was back in the days of home movies, captured on a Super 8 camera; Phil would shoot away and then send the film off to be processed so he could screen his mini masterpieces. That's one thing

I'll give Phil—if he got into a hobby (and there were a few), he wouldn't mess around, he would go for it all out. He progressed from Super 8 to remote-controlled boats, which we'd race on the Serpentine in Hyde Park. But once he saw Ritchie Blackmore's drummer, Cozy Powell, tearing around between gigs in Germany in his Ferrari Dino, that was it for Phil, he was a Ferrari man—when he could afford to become one, of course. That wasn't the case in 1976.

But I genuinely believe that the only way for life to make sense for AC/DC was to keep working. I have no doubt that Mal, Angus and to a certain extent Bon inherited that dour, cut-the-crap immigrant upbringing that was typical of so many Scots who ended up in Australia. I have a few mates who hail from that same post-war influx of Scottish immigrants and one of the many things I admire about them is their lack of bullshit, and their intolerance of the same. Unfortunately, that is sometimes accompanied by bluntness, something that was very evident in the Young brothers.

While we all shared a working-class background, we did differ greatly, personality-wise. Phil and myself were similar, maybe because we were both from Melbourne, but we also shared a strong sense of humour and enjoyed a good time, sometimes excessively so. Hey, we were in a band, why not get out there and get messy sometimes? As for the Youngs, Malcolm was the driven one, and it's my impression that he greatly influenced Angus. Mal was the planner, the schemer, the 'behind the scenes' guy, ruthless and astute, while Angus was more the public face of the Youngs. It's always mystified me that the Youngs have been portrayed as a couple of simple souls in a rock band; in my opinion that's far from the truth. Those guys were and still are very sharp thinkers—

AC/DC's enormous success is testament to that. As with all of us, they may have lacked a bit of formal education but they both learned a lot on the job.

Mal and Angus were very guarded guys, almost to the point of suspicion. I've seen words like 'paranoia' and 'insular' bandied around regarding those two, but I think that's off the mark. Mal and Angus certainly weren't the most sociable guys on the planet but I believe that they were basically very private people who found themselves drawn into a career where savouring your privacy isn't the norm. They never kissed arse or 'networked', which a lot of musicians did in order to move up the ladder. I respected that.

Then there was Bon, a gentleman with old-school manners but a wild side that would appear after a few charges went down, or as gig time approached. Bon was by nature outgoing, friendly and very protective of others. That was tempered by a recklessness that could border on the self-destructive. He also suffered bouts of loneliness. I once heard it said that Bon 'was a great bunch of guys', but that's a bit flippant for me. Bon was a chameleon; he could pretty much fit into any situation he found himself part of. He'd charm the pants off anybody, too, if he was in the mood. He once called himself 'a wolf in wolf's clothing'. Maybe he was right. And like the rest of us, Bon wanted to be part of the 'biggest band ever'.

We were all in an unusual situation: with most workmates, if you were away from the office or the workshop you wouldn't necessarily spend a lot of time together, but we had no choice—we were all living in the same house, for one thing. So as you can imagine it could get a little claustrophobic, a bit tense—here was this bunch of very different personalities thrown together in a band, in a new city, not working, with a lot of time on our hands.

London offered up plenty of interest to Phil and myself, and we set about becoming tourists. Mal and Angus weren't as keen; at the very most they opted for a bit of sightseeing. Michael Browning handed us fifty quid each 'walking around money' every week, and we'd drop that shopping on the King's Road in Chelsea, Kensington High Street and Oxford Street, scoring new jeans, T-shirts, boots and the rest of it. We were all keen on the 'walking around money' concept; that amount would double when we finally hit the road. We also got into the rehearsal studio a few times to clear the cobwebs and ensure our gear was in working order after being air-freighted halfway around the world. Mal, Angus and myself developed a thing for tandoori chicken, to the point where we found ourselves with turmeric-tinged fingers which complemented the nicotine stains on the Young brothers' smoking hands nicely, they had a sort of tone-on-tone thing going on there. Very attractive. But work-wise, April 1976 passed with us very much in a holding pattern.

Financially we were okay, living comfortably enough in one of the world's most expensive cities. Michael Browning managed the finances, so we were basically self-funded and not hitting up the record company every five minutes for an advance. We had all had a good year in '75; even the non-writers in the band (Phil and myself) had a healthy bank balance and the financial freedom to do pretty much as we wanted, within reason. Even though I was a non-driver, I always joked that the first car I was going to buy was a Rolls-Royce. I might as well travel in comfort as a passenger, right? I was pleasantly surprised to discover I could afford a very tidy used Roller if I wanted—paying someone to drive it would be another matter, of course. I didn't have a licence. Still don't.

Bon decided to break the boredom and strike out on his own, as he usually did, renewing some old friendships on the north side of London. He was not one to be tied to the band when he didn't have to be; he seemed ready to hit the escape hatch at a moment's notice. He was also a few years older than the rest of us, which did set him apart a little bit. Bon needed his space and privacy to pursue his particular lifestyle without scrutiny, unwanted interference or criticism. When it wasn't necessary for him to be around, he was gone. Bon would hit the door and at a very decent pace, too—no 'see you later' or 'anyone up for a drink?' Bon was just gone.

Bon decided to visit a pub in Finchley that he used to frequent when he was based in London with the band Fraternity. It wasn't a good move, as it happened. Bon walked in and was on his way to the bar when someone remembered him from what must have been a previous skirmish. The guy walked over and clobbered Bon on the head with a pint glass, one of those heavy jobs with a handle. Welcome back to Finchley, Bon.

Bon said he didn't see it coming; after all, he hadn't been in the pub for years. God knows what he did to the guy in the first place. I guess we'll never know. The blow broke Bon's right cheekbone and put him in hospital. He needed an operation to set the bone properly. Bon was often asked what provoked the attack and he gave the same answer every time. He maintained he was an innocent bystander and had absolutely nothing to do with the brawl he'd walked into. Bon also felt there may have been a touch of karma involved because of all the shit he'd gotten away with in the past.

Bon took great delight in describing the gruesome operation required to fix his face. His cheekbone had been pushed downwards; he must have really been smashed with a fair amount of force. So the surgeon made an incision on his hairline, inserted a probe with a hook attached, grabbed the bits of cheekbone and pulled them back up into the correct position. Then they put him back together. It looked and sounded very painful to me.

But Bon was used to calamity. Before joining AC/DC he endured a long stay in an Adelaide hospital after a near fatal motorcycle crash. Bon was always willing to show me the bloodstains on the inside of his black leather bike jacket, courtesy of that smash. It was a favourite jacket of his and showed up in quite a few photos over the early years. It was a funky black leather number; Bon had sewn fake leopard-skin patches on the shoulders. He was handy with a sewing needle, that boy.

Anyway, he finally got out of hospital after getting his face readjusted and spent a lot of time in his new bed at Inverness Terrace. Coral would come by to take care of him and drop off some homemade soup and a new batch of comics. *Conan the Barbarian* was a constant at the time and Johnnie Hart's *BC* was a newfound favourite. Bon was very big on comics. That's one memory of Bon that comes to me quite regularly: his head buried in a comic book, reading with intent if it was *Conan* or having a good giggle if he was reading *BC*. Bon was also an avid letter writer, he was always knocking out postcards or letters to family and friends, keeping them up with news from the front—or should I say, his front.

Here's an odd thing about my relationship with Bon. I can be exposed to all kinds of Bon-related stuff—video clips, songs, photos, pretty much all things Bon—and it doesn't affect me much at all. Yet when I look at his handwriting it really knocks me around; even something reprinted in a book catches me. If it's an original card, or a letter in his handwriting, it can floor me. I'm not sure what that all means, but if you work it out let me know.

My other strongest memories of Bon are his laugh and his cheeky grin. You know the grin, where you can't help but think he was either up to mischief or had just gotten away with something. That was a hell of a grin. I took a photo of Bon that captures it perfectly; I shot it after a gig, as he was getting into the back seat of a car. It was before all his 'Donny Osmond' dental work; he's wearing that broken grin but it's a beauty nonetheless. Very real.

Bon's dental work was performed by a Harley Street specialist in November 1976. Bon's new smile didn't come cheap: I heard the figure £2000 bandied around, a massive amount considering what we were living on. But Bon was very particular about his appearance. Despite the image of him as this unkempt rock and roll wild man, he was always squeaky clean, and I know his teeth were giving him a bit of grief. I'm not sure they were in tiptop condition before his bike accident so biting the bitumen couldn't have been good for his choppers. No one was surprised when he laid down a stack of cash to get a new smile. But it did take some getting used to. Someone remarked that he looked like Mr Ed, which I thought was rather unkind although pretty funny. It was also around this time that Bon was copping more than a few snide remarks, mostly about his choice of friends and his domestic situation with his girlfriend Silver Smith.

Silver and Bon reconnected not long after we shifted to the UK, but I believe they shared a past that dated back to Bon's Adelaide days. She was about the same age as Bon—that is, a bit older than the rest of us—and came with such added extras as a very cosy flat on Gloucester Road in West Kensington and a retinue of interesting friends, Rolling Stone guitarist Ron Wood among them. Silver's place suited Bon perfectly, giving him sanctuary and a little breathing room from the rest of us.

Bon enjoyed his creature comforts; there was a little bit of the hippie to the guy, and his relationship with Silver was about as comfortable as Bon wanted to be. In no way am I implying the guy was ready to settle down, but there was a laid-back side to Bon, for sure. Silver was an undeniably intelligent woman; cool, relaxed and worldly, traits that weren't in plentiful supply back at the AC/DC house. I'm not sure whether the band held Silver at arm's length or vice versa, but she didn't seem to have any real desire to spend much time with us. Truth be told, apart from Bon, we had fuck-all in common.

There was a set of studio publicity shots taken just after Bon got out of hospital. He was wearing a set of white leather tails he had custom made—how else could you get white leather tails but bespoke?—and a pair of Ray-Ban wrap-around sunglasses. It was obvious why he was wearing the sunnies: the right side of Bon's face was still very swollen and the wraparounds hid a couple of shiners, which were the aftermath of the corrective surgery. Those doctors could be rough.

While Bon was convalescing upstairs at Inverness Terrace—he hadn't shifted in with Silver yet—Phil, Mal, Angus and I lost ourselves in many lengthy late-night poker games. It was one of the rare occasions that Angus would socialise with the band—he was much more likely to be hidden away in his bedroom with his ciggies, cups of tea and Gibson SG. He wouldn't venture out with the rest of us to a pub or a club. It just wasn't his style.

A large ball of hash fuelled one particular card game. Not for me or Angus, though—he didn't drink or take drugs, while I was a Scotch and Coke kind of guy and not a dope smoker. I recall the night vividly because it was the only time I ever pulled a royal flush, all diamonds—and to top it off it was the hand I was dealt. I didn't have to discard anything. It's almost impossible, it's like winning the lottery, and even more satisfying when another player thinks you are bluffing, as was the case.

At one point during the game Phil needed to take a piss break. A few minutes later there was an awful scream coming from what I thought was upstairs. I was sure it was Bon—maybe he was in trouble—so I bolted up to his room only to be greeted by a very sleepy, very self-medicated lead singer.

'What the fuck are you pricks up to down there?' he yawned.

So who was it? I went looking for Phil. I knocked on the toilet door—I could hear him in there but he gave no response, so I forced the door open. He was as stiff as a board, lying on the floor. I thought he was having some sort of fit, so I asked him to stick his tongue out, but he couldn't. So I just grabbed and held onto his tongue because he was making some weird noises. Eventually he came around, but he was whiter than all of us combined. That was definitely the end of the night's poker game.

I offered to make Phil a cup of tea, but by the time it was ready he was out like a light. I guess that he passed out in the toilet and when he came to he was completely disoriented and just didn't know where he was. I have had that happen to me when I have been in that half awake/half asleep zone and panicked—it can be real nasty until you clear your head. Phil didn't admit it at the time, probably because he couldn't talk, but the hash definitely did a job on him. It didn't affect his future intake, though; he was very resilient and was puffing up large, as normal, the very next day. So ended another interesting night in the Inverness Terrace household of AC/DC.

All up, Bon needed about ten days of recuperation and comic-reading after getting his face fixed, during which time the remnants of Back Street Crawler decided to soldier on with a co-opted guitar player by the name of Geoff Whitehorn, and resurrect what was left of the tour. That was fine by us—we just wanted to get out there and blast Back Street Crawler, and the rest of them, to bits.

Chapter 7

'Who the fuck are these poofs?'

As you can imagine, the death of Paul Kossoff put a serious crimp in our plans to promote *High Voltage*, our first album in the UK. It was a compilation of the band's first two Australian releases, *High Voltage* and *TNT*, and came packaged with what I still consider to be the world's worst album cover. It was some sort of stylised cartoon of Bon and Angus—at least I *think* it was—with loads of pink and green. Whoever came up with that doozy obviously had no feel for what AC/DC was about and I'm mystified that the band approved the design. It was a shocker. Not that Phil or I had any influence or input into such decisions, of course.

The back cover was much more like us; at least it showed some humour. It was a montage of fake letters to the band and group shots. One 'letter' alluded to me being thrown out of a club (not that again) and the owners apologising and thanking me for sending flowers to the hospitalised bouncer. That sort of thigh-slapping humour and image-mongering would normally have me cringing, but compared to the front cover it was a crackerjack piece of work. It was that fucking awful. Thankfully, the US release kept the back cover and ditched the front, instead using an image of the manic schoolboy Angus Young—was there any other kind?—on a plain background with a lightning bolt. It was a hell of an improvement. I was a big fan of the Aussie *High Voltage* cover with the image of the dog lifting its leg on the power box. Now that's what I called a cool cover. The title 'High Voltage' and the cover concept was the brainchild of Chris Gilbey, the A&R man for Alberts back in Sydney.

Our immediate issue, however, was what to with AC/DC while waiting for the remnants of Back Street Crawler to get their act together. The simple answer was to pull some pub dates around London to spread the word about the band and hopefully get some street vibe going. The downtime also gave us the chance to check out some more gigs and to keep sizing up our competition. Seeing that said competition was playing in the pubs and clubs around town it wasn't much of a stretch to round up a search party of Mal, Phil and myself to hit the traps and also test out the local brews. All in the name of research, of course.

It was on one of these research missions that Mal, Phil and I ordered a 'minicab' to take us into the city. Minicabs were everywhere in London; they looked like private cars but the drivers were licensed cabbies. They weren't your traditional black London cabs driven by blokes with outrageous East End accents. The minicab drivers, in general, looked decidedly dodgy and the geezer that rocked up this day was no exception.

During the drive we got into a conversation. Because the guy was Jamaican, Mal and Phil figured he would know where to score some grass. This all happened within the first couple of minutes of our journey; the guys were mighty keen to have a puff. Our driver was happy to help out and yes, he did know a spot just round the corner from where we were going, funnily enough.

We reached the place and handed the driver twenty quid. He locked the car and went into a terrace house. He was gone for fifteen or twenty minutes, while we gut-ached about being ripped off. Finally our guy returned, stoned to the gills. He was a mess, completely whacked and stumbling all over the place. He handed the guys a neat little newspaper parcel, got back into the car and then weaved down Kensington High Street at a snail's pace.

Mal and Phil were suitably impressed; the gear must be good, given the state of our driver. (He's probably still toasted.) But the dope didn't look anything like they had seen before. In fact, to me it looked a lot like some herbs you might use in cooking, so much so that when the guys did smoke it, with zero impact, someone asked what we had for dinner.

The first London club we visited that night was the Speakeasy, a music industry haunt and what was known as a 'showcase' gig. It was tiny, cramped and dark but had a vibe to it. There was every chance you'd bump into members of The Who, a Rolling Stone or any visiting band who were in town and trying to bone the local lassies, something we'd failed at to date.

The evening started strangely, especially for AC/DC. We were sitting at a table with some people from our label, Atlantic, drinking record-company-supplied French champagne. I don't think that French champagne and AC/DC have ever been mentioned before in the same sentence, so there's a first. Our record company escorts were Steve Payne and Sue Patience, promo people, who must have been simply *deeee-lighted* to show off their hometown to a bunch of arrogant little fuckers just off the plane from Orstralia. They did it with smiles on their faces, although I did note that the smiles turned a little thin-lipped at times. Still, we did get along well with Sue, who was friends with Coral, and Steve. Steve and I would later hang out a bit for beer, curries and laughs.

Then the band came on. They were a typical pop/rock/glam outfit, looking like a hangover from the Marc Bolan/Ziggy Stardust school of make-up and high heels. To my ears, they should have spent a bit more time tuning the guitars and less time putting on their lippy. For the life of me I can't remember their name but I can tell you this: they stunk. It was a clear indication that maybe the local 'talent' was not that flash. The champers started to kick in, and Mal very loudly asked Steve Payne, 'Who the fuck are these poofs?' This was met with gales of laughter from the rest of us at the table, though not so much from our new record company buddies, who were actually thinking about signing said poofs. When they sheepishly told us, we answered with uncontrollable sprays of Moët et Chandon. I mean, really, we couldn't help ourselves. They were rubbish.

The Atlantic crew threw a small reception for us at their office on Oxford Street in the city soon after. It was a very low-key affair—come in, get to know the rest of the staff, have a few beers and we'll pretend that we think you're going to be huge. And for us, that was about the band's limit for playing the game. We copped a lot of 'oh, they're soooo natural' during those early days in London, which translated to 'there's no way I'm letting those guys know where I live', so we were happy to keep our distance from most of the so-called taste-makers.

Of course it would have been crazy not to try to get off to a good start with Atlantic, but it wasn't long before I was feeling decidedly uncomfortable and looking to hit the door. Steve Payne, bless him, knew it was a pain in the arse but did his best to put us at ease.

'There is someone that you all must meet,' we were told, and shuffled off to a separate room, where we were assembled into a meet-and-greet line-up.

Who's it going to be, I wondered—the Queen and Prince Philip? I was kind of hoping for Keith Richards; Rolling Stone Records was based in the same building. Instead, this older, very straight-looking guy was ushered in and started making his way along the line.

'This is Malcolm Young, one of the guitar players,' he was told, and so on, down the receiving line. 'This is Angus . . .'

I was thinking: 'Who the fuck is this guy and what the fuck are we supposed to do—curtsy?' Our esteemed guest made his way to Bon, who was introduced as the singer.

Bon couldn't resist and asked the obvious question: 'What do you do around here, mate?'

I swear I heard an intake of breath from the Atlantic staffers.

'My dear fellow'—that's how this guy talked—'I'm Derek Taylor. I worked for the Beatles. You've heard of them, haven't you?' Derek looked around, thinking he was being as witty as Oscar Wilde—shit, he may even have thought he *was* Oscar Wilde.

I was next in line and toasted his wit with a massive beery burp that Mr Taylor/Wilde greeted with a look of utter distaste. He has no idea how close he came to a smack in the mouth, poor sod.

We had acquired an agent in London, a chap named Richard Griffiths, a very refined fellow who stuck out like a sore thumb when he was with us. Over time, however, we were able to drag Richard down to our level. Richard had just started up his own agency and was hungry, therefore a perfect match for AC/DC. He worked with Back Street Crawler, among others. I got along very well with Richard; he was a welcome new face in my world. He was having some success at the time with Eddie and the Hot Rods, a band that was currently doing well in London. This, naturally, made them a target for us.

'So you've got the best in town, have you, Richard?'

So it was off to the Marquee to see Eddie and his Hot Rods. The Marquee was a famous club in Wardour Street, Soho, that could lay claim to breaking the Rolling Stones, The Who, Jimi Hendrix and Led Zeppelin. Straight away it felt familiar: it was confined, stuffy, dirty, smelly and gritty, just like our Melbourne HQ, the Hard Rock Café. It was a tailor-made new home ground for AC/DC and we'd come to play there more than a dozen times during 1976.

We were all primed to absolutely hate Eddie and the Hot Rods and that's exactly what happened. 'How did this band come to be so hot?' we asked ourselves. When it came to other bands, I was probably the most lenient guy in AC/DC, but even I thought they were crap. They were attempting some sort of frantic R&B, later mastered by Dr Feelgood. 'Are Eddie and his mates using the same songlist?' I asked at one point, which got a few laughs. Truly, to me they didn't sound like they were playing the same song. Richard accepted our criticism as simply good-natured ribbing; he didn't realise that we were deadly serious. So over the course of one night we'd claimed a new home ground and had a target named Eddie and the Hot Rods in our sights.

Our first-up offer of a gig was a cracker, and it came via Coral. She had a friend, Spartacus, who was the bass player in the band Osibisa, and we would play as support to his band. They were some sort of African outfit, playing an amalgam of tribal music and contemporary stuff with a weird mix of instruments. The gig was in Brighton, some hundred kilometres south of London. We were offered the grand fee of ten quid, which wouldn't have covered the cost of petrol. We politely passed. We all had a good giggle about that one, including Richard, who assured us that the next offering would be an improvement. Wouldn't be too hard to top that one.

ϟ

London, thankfully, was an easy town in which to start kicking up some dust. It had a number of well-known clubs and pubs where you could play *and* get noticed by the music papers, *Melody Maker*, *NME* (*New Musical Express*) and *Sounds*, the new rag on the block. That was the perfect way to develop a following.

The Red Cow in Hammersmith, however, was not one of these well-known gigs. But that is where we played our first London gig, a free one, on 23 April 1976, set up by Richard. The Red Cow was on Hammersmith Road, which ran parallel to the Hammersmith flyover, a raised sort of freeway eyesore that was supposed to make getting in and out of the city easier, but at a great cost to the local landscape. It was a tiny pub with an even tinier stage (lucky we were all tiny ourselves). Capacity was probably around 150, and even then everyone was packed in like sardines.

We were running it like a Melbourne pub gig, a format we were well accustomed to—there was a set from a support band, then two sets from us. We were all super keen to start playing again; it had been a massive lay-off for us, almost a month since our 'farewell' show, a full house at the Bondi Lifesaver, so we would have been willing to play in a toilet. We'd worked non-stop in Australia, pausing just long enough to record *TNT* and *Dirty Deeds Done Dirt Cheap*, but the only playing we had done recently was a couple of run-throughs at a disgusting rehearsal studio on the King's Road in Chelsea. It was a dank, nasty dump that smelled like mushrooms. For once I welcomed the guys' dope smoking; it took the edge off the stench.

Gig time at the Red Cow was approaching and the crowd, if you could call it that, was very thin. There were maybe thirty people in the room. We didn't care, we were playing again and our vibe was sky-high. Angus, who could be very jumpy before a gig, was as happy as I'd ever seen him. He was vibing and smiling up large, flashing those god-awful teeth of his. ('If there was a white one in there, it would look like a snooker set,' was Pat Pickett's favourite line to describe Angus's chompers.) We were ready, in control of our emotions, as always, but there was this pent-up emotion that was palpable. If I was to point to one moment in my time with AC/DC when we felt like brothers, well, this was it. This really felt like the start of something, even if were playing to thirty drunken punters at the Red Cow. They had no idea what was about to hit them.

We opened with 'Livewire'. My bass intro drifted in the air, Mal's ominous guitar chords joined in, Phil's hi-hat cymbals tapped away and then the song exploded when Angus and the drums absolutely fucking erupted. I felt like I was lifted off the ground, it was that powerful. It just sounded so much like AC/DC. That may seem to be a ridiculous thing to say, but we hadn't played a gig for ages and we were ready to make a statement. There was that great feeling of power; not the chaotic, noisy, out-of-control power that is very common in bands, but the AC/DC brand of power. Loud, clean, deep, menacing and full of rhythm. We were back and firing and Bon hadn't even opened his trap yet.

I noticed Michael and Richard on the other side of the stage (not so difficult, given it was only about five metres across). Michael had a big 'I knew it' smile on his face—and Richard's jaw had dropped open. He was stunned. The rest of the set cooked along. I think we felt a certain amount of relief that we were on our way again, as we kicked out a month's worth of cobwebs.

Our thirty or so new friends from the Red Cow were firing, too; they were well into it. I'm not sure what they made of the barrage but we certainly got their attention. After the first set we were surprised to see people leaving. In fact, most of them disappeared, which did seem strange. The few that remained were refreshing their drinks or making calls on the public phone. We shrugged it off. 'Fucking Poms.'

However, as the second set neared, the crowd started to build up again. The punters that were there at the start had returned with their mates. The place was full by the time we got back on stage. It was an unusual night, very successful for what it was, an odd gig but memorable nonetheless. And I know we scared the daylights out of our new agent. Afterwards, Richard pulled me aside.

'That was the loudest, meanest thing I've ever heard in my life,' he gasped, both thrilled and a little intimidated. 'It was like a monster waking up.'

Clearly we were on our way.

Finally, word came through that the remnants of Kossoff's band, with new guitarist Geoff Whitehorn filling the great man's shoes, were as ready as they'd ever be to tour with us. I don't think it's unkind to say that without their star, the tour was a non-event. However, there were a few key dates for us during that run of shows. May 11 and 12 were set aside for gigs at the Marquee. The venue held about 700 people, but the demand for Back Street Crawler, if 'demand' is the right word, had diminished in the wake of Kossoff dropping off the twig. The crowd on the first night was smallish, but, still, it was the legendary Marquee.

The Marquee might have been a small club, but its band room was positively miniature. We entered via a door at the end of the bar and went through a toilet before reaching the band room. Even with we five midgets in there it was crowded. This was the room where the black and white shots were snapped for the inner sleeve of our *Dirty Deeds* LP, so it has a little history attached to it, as nasty as the dump was.

We were doing the usual thirty-minute opening slot. We'd get on stage, plug in, rip into 'Livewire' and eventually wind up with 'Baby Please Don't Go', where Angus would do his thing in the crowd, creating a nightmare for every roadie we ever worked with—remember, this was long before the day of wireless guitar set-ups. Our two sets at the Marquee went down well enough. There were plenty of 'what the fuck is this?' stares from punters, but we'd grown used to that. After all, we had a leering old bloke out front and a Steptoe-lookalike dressed as a schoolkid attacking his Gibson. What could we expect, really? According to one UK journo, 'The venue's usually somewhat bombed out and refugee-like audience was transformed into a happy and good-humoured one—why, there were smiles on people's faces. If ever there was a good-time band, this is it.' Those Marquee dates opened the door just a crack for us—now it was just a matter of kicking the fucker in.

There was no real relationship to speak of between us and Back Street Crawler. We certainly didn't go out of our way to break the ice and figured that a couple of them were on a bit of a star trip. I'm not sure how playing half-empty clubs justified that, and this kind of ego crap certainly didn't wash with us. But I got on okay with two guys in the band, both, strangely enough, named Terry Wilson. One was the singer, the other the bass player. They were good guys but were working under immense pressure—it couldn't have been easy after Kossoff's death. I mean no disrespect to Back Street Crawler, as they were just trying to hang on after losing their leader, but I don't think anyone was expecting great things from them and that's pretty much what people got. For us, we learned yet again that so-called 'headliners' weren't always all they were cracked up to be.

Cuddling up with my mother, Norma, Murrumbeena, Victoria, 1958. Groovy earrings, Mum.

EVANS FAMILY

Smiling up large with Dad in the backyard, Murrumbeena, 1957.

EVANS FAMILY

In the backyard with my sister, Judy, Murrumbeena, 1959. I still have the same stance, except I'm no longer a lefty, thanks to my first-grade teacher and her ruler.

EVANS FAMILY

Opposite: Concentration plus, Melbourne Festival Hall, 16 June 1975. If anyone finds my Gibson Cherryburst Ripper Bass, I want it back!

EVANS FAMILY

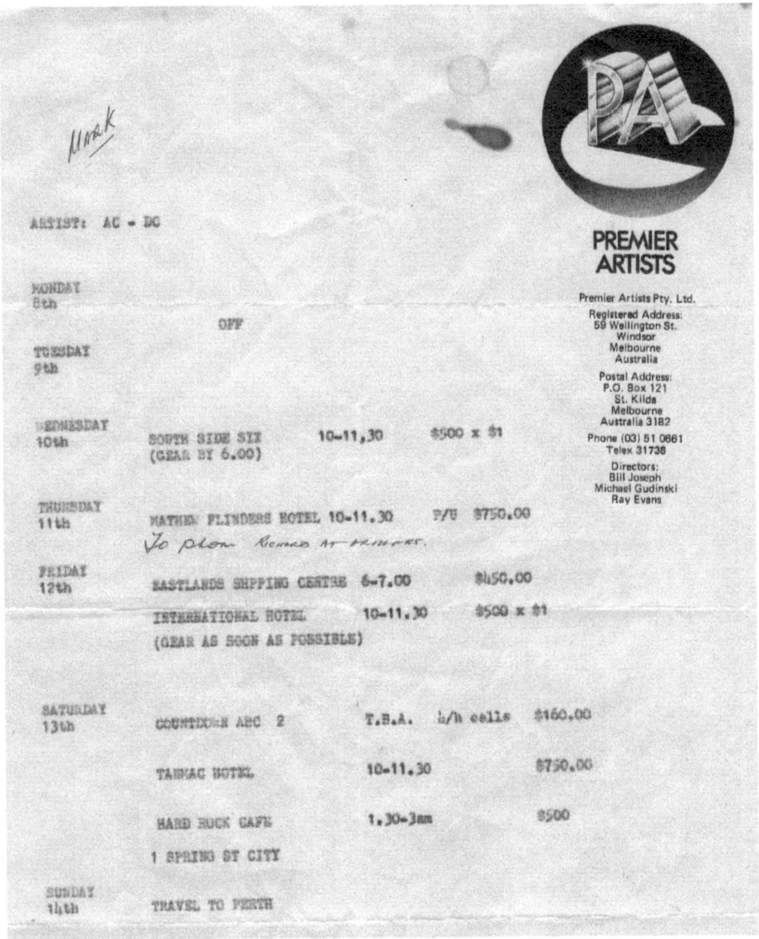

Mark

ARTIST: AC - DC

PREMIER ARTISTS

Premier Artists Pty. Ltd.
Registered Address:
59 Wellington St.
Windsor
Melbourne
Australia

Postal Address:
P.O. Box 121
St. Kilda
Melbourne
Australia 3182

Phone (03) 51 0661
Telex 31738

Directors:
Bill Joseph
Michael Gudinski
Ray Evans

MONDAY 8th				
	OFF			
TUESDAY 9th				
WEDNESDAY 10th	SOUTH SIDE SIX (GEAR BY 6.00)	10-11,30		$500 x $1
THURSDAY 11th	MATHEW FLINDERS HOTEL To plan Records at Premier	10-11.30	P/U	$750.00
FRIDAY 12th	EASTLANDS SHPPING CENTRE	6-7.00		$450.00
	INTERNATIONAL HOTEL (GEAR AS SOON AS POSSIBLE)	10-11.30		$500 x $1
SATURDAY 13th	COUNTDOWN ABC 2	T.B.A.	h/h calls	$160.00
	TARMAC HOTEL	10-11.30		$750.00
	HARD ROCK CAFE 1 SPRING ST CITY	1.30-3am		$500
SUNDAY 14th	TRAVEL TO PERTH			

Band worksheet for the week ending 14 September 1975. The week ended earlier than expected when Phil broke his thumb in a brawl at the Matthew Flinders Hotel.

PREMIER ARTISTS

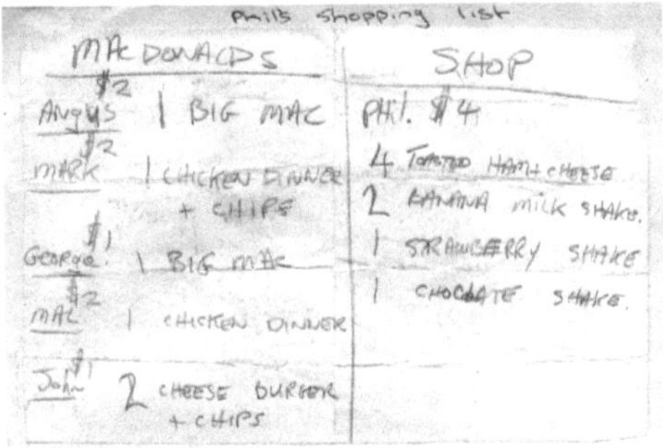

Phils shopping list

MACDONALDS	SHOP
Angus $2 — 1 BIG MAC	PHIL $4
MARK $2 — 1 CHICKEN DINNER + CHIPS	4 TOASTED HAM + CHEESE
George $1 — 1 BIG MAC	2 BANANA MILK SHAKE
MAL $2 — 1 CHICKEN DINNER	1 STRAWBERRY SHAKE
John $1 — 2 CHEESE BURGER + CHIPS	1 CHOCOLATE SHAKE

Phil went on a dinner run for the band during the recording of *Dirty Deeds*. We definitely weren't into health food. The chocolate milkshake has to be for Angus.

KD COLLECTION

Angus, me and Mal during the *Dirty Deeds* sessions at Albert Studio, January 1976.

PHILIP MORRIS

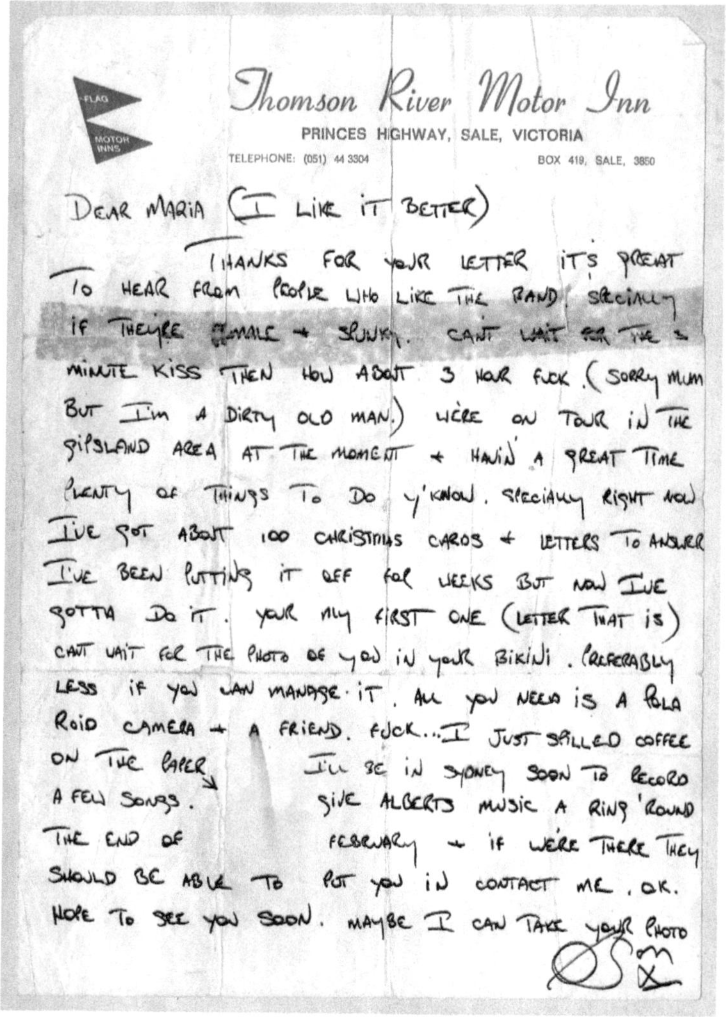

Thomson River Motor Inn
PRINCES HIGHWAY, SALE, VICTORIA
TELEPHONE: (051) 44 3304
BOX 419, SALE, 3850
FLAG MOTOR INNS

DEAR MARIA (I LIKE IT BETTER)

THANKS FOR YOUR LETTER IT'S GREAT TO HEAR FROM PEOPLE WHO LIKE THE BAND, SPECIALLY IF THEY'RE FEMALE + SPUNKY. CAN'T WAIT FOR THE 3 MINUTE KISS THEN HOW ABOUT 3 HOUR FUCK (SORRY MUM BUT I'M A DIRTY OLD MAN.) WE'RE ON TOUR IN THE GIPSLAND AREA AT THE MOMENT + HAVIN' A GREAT TIME PLENTY OF THINGS TO DO Y'KNOW. SPECIALLY RIGHT NOW I'VE GOT ABOUT 100 CHRISTMAS CARDS + LETTERS TO ANSWER I'VE BEEN PUTTING IT OFF FOR WEEKS BUT NOW I'VE GOTTA DO IT. YOUR MY FIRST ONE (LETTER THAT IS) CAN'T WAIT FOR THE PHOTO OF YOU IN YOUR BIKINI. PREFERABLY LESS IF YOU CAN MANAGE IT. ALL YOU NEED IS A POLA ROID CAMERA + A FRIEND. FUCK... I JUST SPILLED COFFEE ON THE PAPER. I'LL BE IN SYDNEY SOON TO RECORD A FEW SONGS. GIVE ALBERTS MUSIC A RING 'ROUND THE END OF FEBRUARY + IF WE'RE THERE THEY SHOULD BE ABLE TO PUT YOU IN CONTACT ME. OK. HOPE TO SEE YOU SOON. MAYBE I CAN TAKE YOUR PHOTO

Bon
X

Bon's letter to a very keen fan, it would seem . . .

KD COLLECTION

Opposite: Sydney Festival show at the Haymarket, 30 January 1977.

BOB KING

AC/DC

SPECIAL REPORT

They oughta be locked up!

ALL THE chicks love AC/DC — that bunch of spunky rockers.

Wherever the boys go they are hounded by their hundreds of female fans.

When Bon and Angus start gyrating around the stage the wild, frenzied screaming starts and keeps going until the boys leave the stage.

Malcolm, Phil and Mark also get their share of the screams, and it's little wonder.

Hundreds of girls are in love with the boys from AC/DC.

Following is a typical letter from an AC/DC fan. The boys get bags full of letter like it.

Dear Fellas:

Ever since your concert in Toowoomba you have been my favorite group.

I can't get over how sexy and horny Malcolm Young is. Boy, would I like to have it off with you, Malcolm.

You are the spunkiest. If you are ever in Toowoomba again . . .

Forget that, I don't want you to think I'm a slut or anything.

I reckon Bon Scott is really horny too, so is Mark and Phil. Angus is funny.

I hope you all believe what I say.

If you are in Toowoomba again I'll be the one who jumps up on the stage and goes for Malcolm instead of like last time when I just yelled out and got a wink.

Next time I'll get more than a wink.

Love from . . .

We've left out the name of the girl who wrote this letter so she won't get embarrassed.

But it's just like the ones sent to those spunk-rockers AC/DC every day.

Incarcerated in the Old Melbourne Gaol for a teen music fanzine, June 1975. Seemed like a good idea at the time . . .

SPUNKY MAGAZINE, NO. 24, KD COLLECTION

Photo shoot for 'Jailbreak', Lavender Bay, Sydney, March 1976. Our manager, Michael Browning, is the big copper on the right.

PHILIP MORRIS

Getting a warm London welcome at WEA Records: Bon and myself trying a pincer movement on Cherry from the PR department (unsuccessful), April 1976.

DICK BARNATT, WWW.BARNATT.COM

Marshall

Our first major London gig: Angus and me at the Hammersmith Odeon, 10 November 1976.

DICK BARNATT, WWW.BARNATT.COM

Opposite: Bon putting on the moves and making up for lost time—he'd caught the wrong train to our gig at the Hammersmith Odeon.

DICK BARNATT, WWW.BARNATT.COM

Previous spread: Nashville Rooms, London, 3 June 1976. The gig got reviewed in *NME* under the headline 'I Wallaby Be Your Man'.

DICK BARNATT, WWW.BARNATT.COM

Sydney Airport 'Welcome Home' press conference, 26 November 1976. Bon looks thrilled. Worse was yet to come on tour.

PATRICK JONES, WWW.PJSTUDIO.COM.AU

Record reception, Melbourne, 6 December 1976. That's our den mother and PR person, Coral Browning, holding a platinum record for *TNT* while we are holding her. Nice work if you can get it.

FAIRFAX

Copenhagen, Denmark, 19 April 1977. Angus and me with my 1954 Fender Precision Bass. Didn't know it but it was my last gig with the guys.

JORGEN ANGEL, WWW.ANGEL.DK

The Sydney Showgrounds after-gig party: Mal, me, Brian, Phil and Ted Albert with a shitload of gold and platinum records, 23 February 1981.

PATRICK JONES, WWW.PJSTUDIO.COM.AU

In the band room, very early days, Melbourne, April 1975. Left to right: Malcolm, Angus, Bon, Phil and me.

EVANS FAMILY

Angus with his Hagstrom guitar—his Gibson SG took the night off. Hordern Pavilion, Sydney, Australia, 24 December 1975.

KD COLLECTION

George Young at the mixing desk, *Dirty Deeds* sessions, January 1976.

KD COLLECTION

My favourite sleeping spot, the couch in Albert Studio, invaded by interlopers during the *Dirty Deeds* sessions.

KD COLLECTION

Angus with his hands full during the *Dirty Deeds* sessions. How appropriate.

KD COLLECTION

Angus sweating out at a lunchtime schoolies gig at the Hard Rock Café, Melbourne, May 1975.

EVANS FAMILY

Bon making a backseat getaway après gig, Melbourne, May 1975. This is my favourite photo of Bon—it captures his personality perfectly. Love the broken smile, one of a kind.

EVANS FAMILY

Angus and me at the Marquee Club, London, August 1976.

KD COLLECTION

Opposite: Getting hitched in Las Vegas—Elvis, my wife Bille and me, 3 August 1991.

EVANS FAMILY

With Australian football legend Ron Barassi and my buddy Roland McAdam at a Sydney Swans pre-game lunch at the Sydney Cricket Ground, 1996.

EVANS FAMILY

With my best pal, Graham Kennedy, Centennial Park, Sydney, 2004. It's a long way, mate. Graham is Senior Manager Global, Live Events, for the Wiggles . . . Rock and roll!

EVANS FAMILY

Bon's soulmate and companion, Mary Renshaw (nee Walton), me and Irene Thornton (Bon's ex-wife) at Vince Lovegrove's sixtieth birthday, Sydney, 24 March 2008. It was a long night, plenty of alcohol-assisted stories.

DOUG THORNCROFT

The Pat Cash Band at the Bourbon and Beefsteak Bar, Sydney, February 2005. Left to right: Mark Evans, Juno Roxas, Mick Cocks, Sam Righi, Pat Cash and Mick O'Shea.

SAM RIGHI

With Mick Cocks at the Bridge Hotel, Sydney, 24 April 2008, for the launch of Pete Wells's last album, *Bodgie Dada*.

IMAGE FOCUS AUSTRALIA

Disneyland

Celebrating my fiftieth birthday with Kristin. I'm wearing an East Sydney football guernsey and I was looking down the barrel of the World's Worst Hangover. Lilyfield, 4 March 2006.

EVANS FAMILY

Opposite: At home with my girls, Kristin on the left, Ginnie under my wing. This is my favourite shot of us—it is impossible for me to be happier than at that very moment. Lilyfield, Australia, 2001.

EVANS FAMILY

Backstage with Ginnie at the 'One of the Boys' concert for Mick Cocks, Enmore Theatre, Sydney, 24 July 2009.

BOB KING

Kristin waves goodbye. Lilyfield, March 2006.

EVANS FAMILY

On stage with Dave Tice, at the Adelaide International Guitar Festival, 7 December 2009. I was anointed the 'World's Loudest Acoustic Guitar Player'.

TIM KOWALICK, TK EVENTS, WWW.TKET.COM.AU

On 28 May we played Surrey University. We went on with our usual attitude but the punters just stood and stared. They all sat on the dance floor, and didn't do so much as get off their backsides, even though we were playing loud enough to wake the dead. I thought they must have all been whacked; some were even doing the cross-legged thing—and I'm pretty sure I saw a caftan or two, which was never a good sign for AC/DC. It would have been pretty funny except for this: the head of Atlantic Records, *the* top guy, Ahmet Ertegün, was at the gig.

Ahmet Ertegün was a legend. He *was* Atlantic Records. He'd founded the label just after World War II and had signed such legends as Ray Charles and Aretha Franklin, gradually moving from jazz and R&B to rock and roll. Not only did he have Led Zeppelin, his roster also included Crosby, Stills, Nash & Young, Emerson, Lake & Palmer, the Rolling Stones, Aretha Franklin, Otis Redding—and now, erm, AC/DC.

So the last thing we needed right now was to stiff at a gig in front of Ahmet Ertegün. Yet that was looking like a distinct possibility, because these fuckers were not moving. They were statues. Stoned statues. Some were now lying on the floor in front of us. 'This is it,' I thought to myself, 'we're fucked.' As usual Bon and Angus charged on—I can't recall a gig where either didn't give it everything and then some—but even as we tore into 'Baby Please Don't Go' the place was more like a library, maybe even a morgue.

Regardless, Angus started up his rave, jumping off the stage and into the crowd. It was probably the only time that he ever waded into the crowd and didn't immediately get swallowed up by eager punters. There was no response from the caftan wearers; zero. But then Angus hit the deck, spinning around, firing out some manic solos and looking like he was fit to be caged. Bang! The hippies around him suddenly jumped up and this started a chain reaction—the whole place was now up on their feet, trying to get a look in, pushing towards the stage and Angus, sucked into the action. They started cheering Angus on, clapping and hooting. It was as if they had all woken from their stoned stupor at the same time. The hippies went absolutely nuts. We left to a thunderous ovation.

We were all well pleased and adjourned to the bar for a meet-and-greet with some Atlantic people. Bon and I were sipping away when Ahmet approached us and introduced himself. Once the pleasantries were finished he apologised for only catching the very end of the show.

'Man, you boys brained them out there,' the suave and sophisticated Mr Ertegün commented. 'They went crazy.'

Bon and I exchanged a grin. Angus had pulled us out of the shit, yet again.

Chapter 8

'Hey guys, ever wondered why they call it dope?'

In the wake of the buzz generated by our Marquee shows, the magazine *Sounds* coughed up some sponsorship pounds and we embarked on the UK version of our Lock Up Your Daughters tour. Michael Browning, along with Coral, put together a deal with *Sounds* to sponsor and heavily promote our nineteen-date tour. As Michael said, 'It's a pretty good score,' and it gave us an excellent leg-up.

It was a double-edged sword, though; we cuddled up nice and cosy-like with *Sounds*, so it was almost automatic that the *NME* and *Melody Maker*, the other two more prominent UK music rags, would take a contrary position. They could be fairly sniffy at the best of times but now they could afford to have a serious look down their noses at us. The general vibe from those two pillars of the British music scene was that we Aussie upstarts were crass, banal, loud and hopelessly out of step with the current trend of punk. *Sounds*, meanwhile, thought we were the best thing since sliced bread. It was an object lesson in not taking to heart what the papers said. And it was hard to take some of the critics seriously, particularly the ones that were trying to put their own bands together. It's like that old joke: One guitar player asks another what he's up to. 'I'm writing songs for my next album.' To which the first replies: 'Shit, I'm not doing anything either.'

There was the occasional mention in the press of Dame Edna, and we did have one article run under the headline ROLL OVER, ROLF HARRIS, but I'll admit that we were treated okay—someone described us as a 'raucous colonial combo', while someone else wrote: 'AC/DC bring entertainment, decadence and good, sweaty fun back into rock and roll.' 'Bon Scott, lead singer, is a character,' noted another writer. 'You'd swear they found him in a loonie bin somewhere and cut him loose.' Bon was also referred to as the 'daddy of the group', closer to the truth than the writer realised. Angus, meanwhile, was called a 'juvenile guitar maestro'.

The *Sounds*/Lock Up Your Daughters tour was our first chance to get out on the road in the UK. We took in Scotland, Wales and some major (and not so major) English cities. The tour itself was very modest in size; the word 'shoestring' aptly describes the actual scope and budget. The gigs featured a DJ—DJ Dave as we called him—who opened the show. While a decent enough bloke, he wasn't an exceptionally charismatic DJ. He would introduce a selection of videos, Rolling Stones and the like, and do his best to set up a vibe for the night.

Our opening gig of the tour was at the City Hall in Glasgow and there was a real whiff of homecoming for the Youngs. I'm sure it was a blast for them to be back in Scotland, and we even spotted a couple of WELCOME HOME banners. I warmed up in a tiny pub around the corner on Sauchiehall Street, charmingly named the Red Hoose. The pub was tiny and so was its clientele. I was standing at the bar having a pre-gig pint, when I took a look around and discovered I was the tallest person in the place. The only other time I've had that experience was standing on stage with the band.

We pulled a decent crowd that first night, but then again it was only fifty p to get into the joint. It was a good start, nonetheless; the punters were pretty rabid, very feisty and loud. From what I could see, no females were let out after dark in Glasgow, at least not to an AC/DC gig. Maybe they'd taken 'Lock Up Your Daughters' literally.

After all the Kossoff/Back Street Crawler drama it was good to be on the road again, and it was doubly good to be away from our digs in London, which, despite its size, was starting to feel a bit snug. There were even some band sightseeing trips, a most unusual occurrence but a lot of fun—and educational, too. The Scotsmen in the group duly filled in we 'Sassenachs' on Scottish history. This basically seemed to revolve around the English invading, marauding all over the place and giving the locals a very thin time of it, and then the Scots doing some first-class arse-kicking in return.

We visited Stirling Castle, which sat high up on a volcanic crag. It's a historically important site that overlooks the battlefield of Bannockburn. Mary, Queen of Scots was crowned there in 1543. We also dropped in on Edinburgh Castle, with refreshments taken in the many pubs on the Royal Mile leading to the castle. That was one of the real pleasures of the tour, getting out with the guys and basically being tourists, while watching Mal, Angus and Bon get back in contact with Bonnie Scotland. I had always wanted to visit Scotland and check out where a number of my good mates came from. I found the history of the country as intoxicating as the beer. I think it would be nigh on impossible not to be taken by the place. We'd stop at a country pub for a bite and a pint, someone would mention that the pub had been on the same site since the 1400s, then we'd take a look around and figure that some of the old cronies propping up the bar had been there all that time.

While in Glasgow we stayed at the Wickets Hotel, just off Dumbarton Road. The hotel was so named because it overlooked what we were told was the only cricket oval in Glasgow. It was a Fawlty Towers sort of place, some old world charm mixed with a fair amount of tat. It was down at the heels but very comfortable and welcoming. And not a Spanish waiter in sight.

We had a rare night off, and some plans were made regarding a few beers or whatever else could be found early in the week in Glasgow. I finished my meal and went upstairs to the first-floor room I was sharing with Phil. Our room was at the end of a wide hallway and looked out onto an old church. It was one of those beautiful Scottish evenings; it was still light even though it was well past 8 pm. It wasn't warm by Aussie standards but still very pleasant. I was straight as a die—not one drink had touched my lips during dinner.

I sat down on my bed to change into my beloved Doc Martens, facing a very large picture window. Phil wasn't around; I was completely alone. The window was open and there was a lovely light breeze blowing, billowing the floor-length curtains. I was taking it all in when something suddenly caught my eye. I looked up and was startled. It was nearing twilight but I could still see clearly in the room, and what I saw was the sketchy but very obvious figure of an old man. He was small, stooped and facing away from me. My immediate reaction was to get out of there, and fast. But I couldn't move. I was stunned. I know I was more than scared, even though it was thrilling at the same time.

Let me say right up front, I'm not one to believe in spirits, apparitions, ghosts, visitations, séances, any of that 'spooky' kind of stuff. I just don't buy it and I'm very suss of those who make a living from 'reading the future'. If they're gifted with such foresight, how come they're not gazing into their crystal ball and dredging up tomorrow night's Lotto numbers? The whole caper begs the question: Why would you want to know the future, anyway? Probably the same people who buy a book and read the last page first—seek help immediately, would be my advice. Now that's off my chest, I can tell you about what changed my thinking, or at least made me leave room for the possibility that there could well be some inexplicable things out there.

I called out to the old bloke in my room a few times, but I have absolutely no idea what I would have done if he acknowledged me or spoke. The old geezer couldn't hear me anyway. He was caught up with something on the far wall, and it seemed to me that he was looking at a painting, or perhaps a series of paintings. He would stand in one place for quite some time then shuffle to his right and start again. He would shift his weight from one side to the other, and was holding his cap in his right hand and scrunching it up. He'd move his cap slightly, rubbing the side of his leg with it. He was monochrome, that's the best way I can explain it. He was wearing what looked like an old coat, and his clothes seemed shabby. It wasn't easy working out exactly what he was wearing, but his clothes certainly weren't well fitting. There was a general shabbiness about his appearance.

I sat frozen on the bed for what felt like about five minutes, although I'm not exactly sure how long I was there. It was enough time for the old guy to move a couple of times to his right, and continue staring at something on the wall. I didn't get a look at his face, I only saw him from behind, and sometimes very slightly from the side. Finally I stood to leave and as I was walking to the door I called out to him again, with no reaction. I went down the hallway to Mal and Angus's room. Angus answered the door. He could see I wasn't quite right. He asked me what was up.

'There's this old guy in my room,' I said. 'No, it's not really a guy, it's a ghost.'

'Fuck that!' Angus replied, and he disappeared straight back into his room and slammed the door, leaving me in the hallway. When I knocked again, he reluctantly let me in, and I told Mal and Angus what I'd just witnessed. At first I'd say they were pretty apprehensive, although the sight of their normally even-keeled bass player trying not to shit himself did suggest something was amiss. It took me some time to work up the nerve to go back into my room, but when I did there was no sign of the uninvited guest.

The next morning I was down at reception and spoke with a female staff member.

'Is there an old guy upstairs?' I asked.

Without missing a beat, she said, 'That would be Jimmy. Don't worry, he won't hurt you, but a couple of times a year he will throw some furniture around.'

She explained that I was staying in what was once a reading room, where the daily broadsheets, a forerunner of newspapers, would be posted on the wall. Jimmy was evidently trying to teach himself to read. He wasn't looking at paintings, as I'd thought. He didn't work for the hotel but lived in quarters in the nearby church. She had been told he was a gravedigger and general help around the church and the grounds.

It's difficult for a guy like me, someone that shit-cans the paranormal, to come to terms with an incident like that. I have no explanation for it, apart from figuring that a moment was being replayed that happened probably a hundred-and-some years past. For the record, that was the first and only time AC/DC stayed at the Wickets.

The tour then wound its way south, into such major centres as Sheffield, Bradford and Liverpool and over to the Isle of Man for a gig at the Palace Lido. I made two major discoveries on that trip over to the Isle: a ferry ride on the Irish Sea can be pretty rough, even in mild weather, and cats on the Isle of Man have no tails. What the fuck is that all about?

The gigs on the Daughters tour were mostly well attended, with the odd shocker (or two). The show at the Liverpool Stadium on 19 June was sparsely attended; there were maybe 150 people in a cavernous (sorry about the dud Beatles pun), ageing, creaky 'stadium', not unlike the old Sydney Stadium at Rushcutters Bay. We went on and, as usual, Bon and Angus went for it like there was a full house and people kicking the doors down to get in on the action. By the end of 'Baby Please Don't Go' we'd converted pretty much everyone there to the cause, judging by their reaction. That was the AC/DC way—get out there, do the hard yards and build a following.

There was another humdinger of a gig the following week, on 23 June, at the Brangwyn Hall in Mumbles, Swansea. It was the same deal as Liverpool: get out there and rip into it, and that's exactly what Bon and Angus did, with the rest of us following suit. They were souls to be converted that night in Brangwyn Hall and converted they were; we had a hundred per cent success rate. From now on, AC/DC had five new fans in Swansea.

The tour's climax was a gig in London on 7 July—AC/DC's first major gig in that very musical city. We dropped into the venue, the Lyceum Theatre, in the late afternoon for a sound check and to get the feel of the room. The crew was going through what was now routine for them. There were eight in the team, comprising our Aussies, Ralph the Roadie and Herc, our lighting guy, who'd been joined by the crew from a company named ESE that supplied our touring PA. They were putting together the PA and lights that had been augmented especially for that Lyceum gig. When we arrived, there was plenty of hustle and bustle getting the gear ready for our sound check. Herc was ten metres up in a cherry picker, rigging the lights, perched on a very high stage, maybe another two metres above the theatre floor. He was rushing to get things done, perhaps not a great idea considering he was working with industrial supplies of electricity.

I was down off the front of the stage with Phil, chatting away, when we saw a flash and heard a massive crack. This sent the cherry picker, with Herc in it, falling forward off the front of the stage. Herc had taken a huge bolt of electricity but was still sufficiently with it to try to protect his head on the way down. He got his arms up in front of his face but when the rig catapulted him down onto the theatre floor the force was too much. His head rocked forward, between his arms, and he face-planted right next to Phil and me with a sickening splat.

Fuck! I was positive we had a dead lighting guy. I just couldn't see how Herc could survive the impact. He'd literally flattened his face on the solid wooden floor and he was face down, not moving. Herc then started making some groaning sounds, gurgling, awful, agonised sounds—but we were all relieved to hear anything at all. Thankfully, he survived. I don't know how, but he did. It says a lot about the mentality of the band that none of us went to visit Herc in hospital. The last time I ever saw him was when he face-planted on the Lyceum floor. But the show must go on, and of course it did, bringing the Lock Up Your Daughters tour to a fitting climax—in more ways than one, not just for Herc, but for me.

During that *Sounds* tour we'd hosted a 'best-dressed schoolboy' competition—one hairy bloke turned up decked out as a schoolgirl—while for the Lyceum show, *Sounds* cheekily invited everyone from Bob Dylan to Rod Stewart and Mick Jagger. The late John Peel, the most respected DJ in the country, did turn up, and sheepishly presented a guitar to the winner of the 'Schoolgirl We'd Most Like To' competition, one Miss Jayne Haynes from Harrow, Middlesex. It seemed as though wherever we looked there were girls with laddered stockings and lollipops stuck provocatively in their gobs. Bon summed up the winner with this comment. 'She was beautiful, really sexy. Garters. Suspenders. I was really lusting for her myself, we all were. But Mark won out. He's just too handsome for me to compete with.' Cheers, Bon—and I will admit that Ms Haynes and I shared a memorable night.

During our set, Angus mooned the crowd, as had become his style, but failed to properly zip up before he turned back to the crowd, and exposed a little more of himself than he'd planned. It was that kind of night. 'This was the most exciting, fun and memorable concert I've attended,' said one reviewer. Who were we to argue?

Overall the tour succeeded in introducing us to a new audience. The general consensus was that we belonged to the old school of rock, acts like Status Quo and the Sensational Alex Harvey Band, rather than the 'New Wave' (if in fact that handle had been coined yet) like the Sex Pistols, the Damned and an ever-growing crew of others only too ready to jump on the punk bandwagon. We'd only been in the UK for two months and we were viewed as being 'out of step'. While a bit condescending, it proved just how far we'd been able to infiltrate the music scene in a short time.

After the Lyceum gig, we were staying at the Russell Hotel on Russell Square, just down the road from the British Museum. By this time Bon was ensconced in the apartment over on Gloucester Road with his girlfriend. He was taking a lot of drugs and there was concern that, given Bon's capacity for living on the edge, he might overdose again on smack, as he had just after I joined the band in late March 1975. While this didn't seem to be an imminent threat there was a massive amount of dope-smoking going on among some in the band.

The particular favourite of the day was the gold-coloured hash that the guys purchased in tennis-ball-sized amounts. I've never been a dope smoker but I sure got passively whacked by this shit in various London cars and apartments. I can still recall the rank smell and the thickness of the smoke; it was as dense as a London fog. This was a situation where Angus and I agreed wholeheartedly—the dope-smoking thing was strictly for hippies.

I had grown up with many dope-smoking mates so it didn't faze me, but Angus could barely tolerate it. As soon as someone sparked up a joint in his vicinity, he'd grumble: 'Fuckin' hippie cunts.' Actually, Angus came out with a great line one night when the smokers were giving it a good nudge on a trip back to London. After much stoned talk of time travel and outer space, there was a lull in what some thought was a pretty riveting conversation.

'Hey guys,' said Angus, 'ever wondered why they call it dope?'

Anyway, back at the Russell Hotel, it was Bon's birthday and plans were made to meet up after dinner, have some drinks and maybe hit a club or two. Even Angus was up for it, which was unusual for the band's resident hermit. Fifa from Alberts was in town for a welcome visit.

We were in the bar listening to another enthralling episode of 'The World According to Angus Young' and for some unknown reason we were being thrilled by the details of the Beatles tour of Australia in 1964. In particular, Angus was banging on about the Sydney concert at the old Rushcutters Bay Stadium, which he evidently attended. Now Angus is a little older than me; he entered the world on 31 March 1955, which placed him at nine years old when the Beatles toured. While it's possible that he was there, I guess he sensed that I thought his story was a load of crap, particularly after I started asking a bunch of questions, basically to wind him up. Winding Angus up was a competitive pastime for some and enjoyed by many. It was generally good-natured ribbing, as it was on this night, or so I thought.

It started getting a little testy when I asked him about the ticket price.

'It was four dollars fifty,' Angus insisted.

Now I started pushing him a bit more, just messing around, but Angus was clearly getting the shits with me.

'That was a lot of money for a nine-year-old,' I said. 'Did you buy a program, too? How did you get there—bus or train?'

On I went, even when Malcolm gave me his standard 'shut the fuck up' look, which I was more than accustomed to. By this stage I was certain it was all bullshit (I was wrong, by the way) and kept on about the ticket price, getting him to reconfirm that it was four dollars fifty.

'I should know, arsehole,' snapped Angus, 'because I paid for the fuckin' thing myself.'

I couldn't help myself.

'How come,' I asked, 'it was four dollars fifty to see the fuckin' Beatles in 1964 when we didn't even have decimal currency until 1966? Shouldn't you be talking pounds, Angus, not dollars?'

That was it. From that moment on, Angus had a super-sized version of the shits with me—and he could be an angry little fellow when you rattled his cage. I was firmly in Little Albie's sights for the evening. I could have done the sensible thing by shutting the fuck up and letting it be, but I was a half-pissed twenty-year-old smartarse. Things were getting a little tense as the night wore on. More drinks were consumed and there was still no sign of our guest of honour.

It was now 10 pm and Mal, Angus, Phil, Michael Browning,

Fifa and I had moved into the cosier lounge area. It was pretty clear that Bon was a no-show. I was sitting next to Fifa, chatting away, when Angus mentioned another Alberts' employee, who was not particularly liked by the band, for reasons I don't recall. I was pissed off with Angus and remarked, 'Hey, Angus, you know we don't like him,' which, upon reflection, was unwise and just plain rude. It was Fifa's work colleague and it put her in an uncomfortable position, something she didn't deserve. I was a jerk and being sloshed was no excuse for bad manners.

The next thing I knew, Angus jumped up and punched me in the face—wham, just like that. While there was no damage done I was dead keen to wring his scrawny neck. Michael and others restrained me as I yelled at Angus to take a free shot. Malcolm had now lined up with Angus, as you would expect.

That didn't deter me as I didn't rate either as a physical threat but I'm glad it didn't go further. I'm grateful that Michael was there to calm me down; I'd completely lost my mind by this stage. I've wondered if Angus ever realised how close he came to getting a serious hiding. I really wanted to throttle him. That feeling passed, of course, but it would become apparent to me that some residual ill-feeling lingered. To this day I feel that my future with the band—or lack thereof—was decided over that incident, which tipped things over the edge.

I went up to my room, which I was sharing with Phil (as usual), to pull myself together. It wouldn't have taken much to set me off again. Michael came up to check on me and I was that angry I was shaking. I made the decision to leave for Brighton the next morning to visit a girlfriend for a few days. We were off to Europe in about a week, I'd catch up with the band then. Michael laid some extra cash on me for the trip and asked me not to take any action that I would regret. I admired Michael for that; it was one of the few times in my stint with the band that I felt someone was looking out for me. That night at the Russell Hotel was a massive mistake on my behalf, but Michael helped me get through it, although I think we all suspected it would get tougher for me. And it did soon enough.

Coral had found us the perfect new HQ at 23 Lonsdale Road in Barnes, just over the Hammersmith Bridge. That bridge just so happened to have two pubs as bookends, the Harlequin on the Hammersmith bank and the Bridge Tavern on the Barnes side, both perfectly placed for an evening stroll and a few pints. Lonsdale Road follows the course of the River Thames on the west bank and I have many fond memories of the area, most of them from time spent in pubs, which says loads about my lifestyle.

Carlsberg Lager, one of the very few English beers then available 'chilled', was my fave, along with the obligatory Scotch and Coke. I use the word 'chilled' advisedly; it really meant the bottle sat on a slightly refrigerated shelf so the bottom couple of inches were just about drinkable. But it's amazing what you can get used to. The shelves were similar to the refrigerated trays where glasses were stored in Melbourne pubs. In fact, a Melbourne beer glass was colder than a 'chilled' beer in a London pub.

Our home in Barnes was a stately place with bedrooms for everyone. Phil won the lottery for the master bedroom, which even came with its own bathroom. Phil's room was upstairs, at the front of the house, and it was massive compared to the other bedrooms. We all envied the guy.

Bon, meanwhile, was shacked up with Silver. I had the feeling he wanted to be free to pursue his own thing without interference from anyone, least of all the guys in the band. Michael Browning always held the view that Bon was very aware of his limits. I agree, but there were times when Bon really gave those limits a severe testing. When Bon was with us he gave everything needed, on stage and off, but he was always ready to cut out whenever the opportunity arose. Unlike the rest of us, Bon had a life away from the band, something he very much needed.

Bon and Silver Smith's place on Gloucester Road was disparagingly labelled the 'Hippie Haven'. Silver was viewed with suspicion by some, contempt by others, as was anyone that came close to the band's inner circle. I don't know that anyone, especially a woman, would have been welcomed into the fold—with the exception of Coral and Fifa—although some cooking and home comforts would have been warmly accepted. But this was certainly not forthcoming from Silver; it would have been the last thing on her mind, in my view.

I don't know if she cared for the rest of the band at all, but I'd take a stab and say she couldn't have cared less. Bon was her focus, they had their shared lifestyle—he just happened to be the singer in AC/DC. Bon and Silver were referred to as 'Rod and Britt', a sly reference to Rod Stewart and Britt Ekland, the jetset rock and roll couple of the mid-seventies. Of course we all envied them—the rest of us were very single.

Female-company-wise, it was a dry time for all of us—bar Bon, the shifty fucker—in London. It was in stark contrast to what we were used to in Australia, which was basically:

'Ladies, we will be with you as soon as possible.' AC/DC currently meant less than nothing, and without our trump card, the band's rep, we were out of luck. Fortunately, Phil and I eventually linked up with a couple of staffers at Atlantic to break the drought.

I did suffer the occasional pang of homesickness, but nothing that I would share with the rest of the guys; that just wasn't the done thing. I was missing my pals back home, guys like Graham Kennedy, who'd normally be along for the ride, sharing the experience. I was missing the footy, too, but that turned out to be a blessing as Carlton was entering the doldrums. It's funny—I had no shortage of things to do in London, and would write home and share the news with my pals in Melbourne (and Glynis, my ex), but I wouldn't share my new discoveries and experiences with the other guys in the band. Not that we didn't get on, but we had to deal with the pressure of living in each other's pockets. AC/DC's siege mentality could get exasperating. What we did have in common was the band, and other than that, not a lot.

So, there we were, an odd assortment thrown together on the other side of the world, living and working in very close confines. It's amazing that we got away with it as long as we did. By nature the band, and I really mean Angus and Mal, was stand-offish, and that was how it had been from my first meeting with the guys in Melbourne. This was certainly not Bon's natural inclination, nor mine or Phil's either. But Phil and I fell into step; as passive as that sounds, it was probably the wisest path to take. For me there was also a sense of self-preservation, although history shows that didn't work out so well. I felt it was necessary to stay in line with the AC/DC way of thinking—it was really the band's way or no way at all. I had my pals around me in Melbourne but I hadn't lived with the band until necessity dictated that I do so in London. Phil had been living with the guys since joining, but this us-against-the-world notion was new for me.

It's one thing to be on the road with your crew and entirely another to be coming off the road after a tour and sharing the same house. That much-needed break away from the guys after a serious run of dates just wasn't an option any more. It proved to be much easier on the road—at least I could hide, or lose myself with a newfound friend, especially if my new chum was an accommodating young lady.

At our first gig at the Nashville Rooms in West Kensington, late May 1976, I met a girl named Polly Paul, an expat Aussie, and for the first time in my life got hit by the thunderbolt. Maybe it was more a case of lust at first sight, but that was good enough for me, and things progressed from there. Polly was a tiny girl from Melbourne, with braided blonde hair, who just absolutely floored me. She was a stunner, loads of fun. I was head over heels, seriously smitten, and after a couple of weeks I was in mortal danger of terminal dehydration.

After a gig in Birmingham, Phil and I struck out for London. Phil took the wheel for what he'd term 'low flying'. Phil was equally keen to visit a new and very close female friend, and didn't spare the horses. That guy drove like no one else I'd met. Of course, the thought hadn't occurred to me that Polly would be less than thrilled to see me. When I arrived unannounced, it was basically a case of: 'Mark, the queue starts to the left.' Oh well.

We had acquired some road crew—Ian Jeffrey, our new front of house guy, and Paul 'Scotty' Wright, who was acting tour manager. Both joined us via ESE. Scotty and I became quite close; we really buddied up, and that was a lot of fun but quite unsettling in some ways. Mistakenly thinking that AC/DC was a democratic beast, Scotty was very open with his thoughts and opinions. And via Scotty, I started hearing rumblings that all was not well with my role in the band. Scotty would be privy to conversations and then report back to me. One of the early dispatches related to my stage sound: 'Your bass sound is a bit too much Led Zeppelin; it should be more rock and roll.' This was the first of many second-hand messages I received.

It was also felt that my time on the road could be better spent concentrating on the gig rather than partying. In hindsight, that one was smack on target. While I was dedicated to the band and the guys, I was also keen on the idea of having a good drink and finding new friends to play with, to gain some respite from what was quickly becoming a stifling, 24/7 AC/DC existence. I knew that Bon had the right idea. And I probably should have found some space for myself in our time off. It was difficult to fly under the band's radar when we were stacked into the one house, even one as big as the place in Barnes.

Our place on Lonsdale Road in Barnes was a ripper. It was a double-storey house with plenty of internal room, a spacious living area, and a large backyard, a real rarity in London. It was in a very middle-class part of Barnes just a hundred metres or so from the banks of the River Thames, about 200 metres from the legendary Hammersmith Odeon, a ten-minute walk from the Red Cow, and not far from Barnes

Common. Barnes Common is notorious for having its very own resident apparition named Spring Heeled Jack, who was known to do unspeakable things to young ladies. The house we shared was almost of stately proportions, no doubt the best house any of us had lived in, or even *been* in, for that matter. The place'd have to be worth a couple of million quid these days. The front room was large enough to set up our stage gear.

We agreed it would be good to set an afternoon aside to have a hit-out (sans Bon, of course). I decided to have some lunch before we played, so I hoofed it to the nearby pub. 'Back soon,' I told the guys. I started playing pool at the pub, first for beers and then for a fiver a game. And I swear that I could not miss. Pubs were forced to shut their doors at 3 pm, by which time I was unbeaten and truly toasted. As I stumbled back up Lonsdale Road, still a few hundred metres from home, I could hear that the guys had started without me. They were fucking loud.

I went into the front room and Mal, Angus and Phil were giving it a very decent blast. Mal was playing bass. Mal is a killer rhythm player but he is also a crackerjack bass guitarist, but did look a tad odd playing my blue Rickenbacker 4001—it was almost as big as him. It didn't affect his playing, though; he was on, playing loud, punchy as fuck and totally locked in with Phil, with Angus blowing over the top. It was A-grade stuff.

No one batted an eyelid when I made my unsteady entrance. I decided to settle in and got comfy in the bay window and started to enjoy the music momentarily. Then I pretty much passed out with the guys pounding away at earthquaking volume. True to form they made no mention of my no-show, or the state I was in; it was as though it didn't happen. But I'd just banged another nail into my own coffin.

This front-room jam proved to be a once-only affair, as the neighbours weren't all that thrilled about having an impromptu AC/DC concert ripping along at full throttle. Couldn't say I blamed them, either, although these days I reckon they'd have serious bragging rights. A few handwritten letters were slipped under our door, some politely asking us to cease and desist, others demanding we respect the neighbourhood. But we never laid eyes on any of our correspondents. They were probably scared shitless of we Aussie reprobates.

My new set of mates came out of the nearby council estates, which were very similar to the Prahran Hilton and obviously struck a chord with me. Some of my new pals were even admitted into the cloisters of AC/DC, although they weren't allowed to get too close. Among them was the local dustman, a bloke named Kevin, who had a wonderful Cockney accent. He was from the wrong side of town to have a Cockney accent—Barnes is in West London, in the borough of Richmond upon Thames—but it was a beauty, particularly when he tried to say 'g'day' in a put-on Aussie accent. He'd toss out those rib-tickling jibes much loved by the English: 'What's it like walking the right side up instead of down under?', that kind of thing, which would generate gales of laughter from his fellow Londoners. But Kevin was a nice bloke, so we'd let him get away with it.

Pete Way was the bassist from the UK band UFO, and was also someone I (sort of) got to know. Like Kevin, Pete felt he had a great line in Aussie jokes—at least *he* couldn't stop laughing. Strangely, he would always introduce me to others as Billy Thorpe. To be honest, it's a wonder he even knew who Billy Thorpe was. Perhaps he actually thought my name was Billy Thorpe. Bon did seem to relate to Pete, make of that what you will. (Mind you, Bon started out by calling me Mike, so maybe they bonded over their mutual misunderstanding. Who knows?)

Some of my other new friends in London really pushed it. Don't get me wrong, they were great company, but rather keen on a pharmaceutical or two, and seemed to like giving it a nudge. Bon and I were both getting to know guys like these independently of the band, and these friendships were looked on with some suspicion by AC/DC's inner sanctum.

Still, there was the odd moment of humour and acceptance. The dustmen, especially my mate Kevin, breathed a bit of fresh air into life at Barnes, at least for me. Very early one morning, Mal stuck his head out a window and sang a rendition of 'My Old Man's a Dustman' to the passing garbage truck. That's how I knew the garbage men were cool in the collective eyes of the band. For Mal, that was a real statement.

Our local pub was the Bridge Tavern, on the corner of Lonsdale Road and Castelnau. It was the first pub you came to when you got off the Hammersmith Bridge. This was where the dustmen drank. It was a typical English pub, with darts and warm beer, although they did offer some chilled Carlsberg after much Antipodean gut-aching. The Bridge Tavern had an added attraction—quite a few young ladies hung out there. This caused some friction between us and the local lads. To them we were interlopers who were trying to screw their girls, an assumption that was spot-on. There were a few hiccups here and there but the dustmen were always on hand to smooth things over.

The Bridge was where we made our first attempts to fit in with the locals—except for Angus, that is, who stayed at home drinking tea, smoking ciggies and playing his beloved Gibson well into the night. The neighbours should have thanked the lord he didn't practise with an amp, although his continuous stamping on the floor to the tempo of a marathon-length guitar solo could be distracting.

Angus seemed to resist virtually all social contact outside the band—he even passed on the free tickets we scored to see the Rolling Stones at Earls Court. I figured that Angus didn't want to be seen to be enjoying another band, even if they were the Stones. I felt that he was being unreasonable; not that I cared whether he went or not, but it was a fine opportunity to see a great band, and at no cost! Instead he was his usual taciturn self, dismissive of anyone who showed any interest or excitement about the Stones. Strange, really, considering he was in a band that was playing a bunch of Stones covers only eighteen months earlier. For the record, I enjoyed the gig but I didn't mention that to Angus. It wouldn't have been worth the attitude and aggravation.

Angus had his views and opinions and I had mine; they didn't coincide too often but I do know we agreed on one matter: at this moment in time we were playing in the only band we wanted to be in, AC/DC. Just before we left Sydney, I said to our good mate Ted Mulry that the only way I would leave AC/DC would be in a box. I was dead serious. In 1976 I could never have envisaged life without the band, as tricky as it sometimes got. When we got on stage and ripped it up, nothing else mattered.

I've read plenty about friction between Angus and me. But I never really felt it. If Angus did have issues, he certainly never confronted me about it. There was the occasional flare-up, but I can't recall a member of the band or the crew who wasn't in Angus's firing line at some stage, his brothers included. When things got sticky with Angus, I'd let the dust settle and then approach him, usually with an offer of a cup of tea, and try to sort things out. You had to pick the right time with Angus; the window of opportunity was sometimes very small and as time went on it seemed to be getting smaller, at least for me. I always tried to give Angus a lot of room. He was a complex fellow, a great guy to be around when he was 'on'. The guy was and is an unbelievable talent and the success he's had proves that.

If Angus did have a problem, I'd say that he resented anyone who didn't share his dedication. He operated on a very high level and would not accept any less from others. I believe it frustrated him when others, me included, didn't perform to his expectations. And I'm not talking about whirling around the stage like Angus; I'm talking about the level of intensity that he felt was necessary to bring it on stage (and in the studio). Let me tell you, Angus set the bar very high indeed.

I believe that dedication was at the heart of any issues Angus may have had with me, but like I said, it was never discussed. On a few occasions I tried to clear the air with Angus and Malcolm, but never at the same time. Typically, they'd say, 'Oh, that's Mal, not me,' or, 'You know what Angus is like, don't worry about it.' After some time in the band I really felt that I was getting fucked around. I wanted to be reassured of my place, but the best I was getting was lip service.

Still, the time spent in the house in Barnes was my happiest with the band. There was plenty going on and we were on the way up; we started to feel really good about our UK prospects. And just being in London was a blast. I was on the tube and into the city on a regular basis. I picked up some bass guitars from a store named Orange Music in Denmark Street. I bought a cracker of a 1954 Fender Precision bass and a 1964 Gibson Thunderbird II. And I also bought my all-time favourite bass, a white 1966 Fender Precision with an Olympic White finish and a maple cap neck. I've still got it and it works a treat. I paid £120 for it at Macari's Music on Charing Cross Road. I love that bass. (Even now, dedicated AC/DC fans still offer to buy it; the last offer I refused was for US$25,000.) I almost parted company with my trusty Fender Precision at one point but got spooked just before the deal was completed. A very keen Californian-based AC/DC fan and avid collector, Aaron Baker, made an extremely generous offer that I accepted, but prior to shipping I found I just could not part ways with my dear old friend. Aaron was extremely gracious, allowing me to back out of the deal and he is now a very good (and understanding) friend.

The house in Barnes became the epicentre of entertainment when the band was in town. We even threw a couple of Aussie-style barbecues, complete with a soccer match in the backyard. (Not that Aussie, come to think of it.) Mal always starred but even Angus would have a crack—and he showed some form, too. He was very quick on his feet, as you can imagine, and hard to tag, the little bugger. Mal had a great passion for soccer; he was an avid Glasgow Rangers fan. There was even a Dustmen vs AC/DC game one time. I can't remember who won but then again I wouldn't have been much help, what with my Aussie Rules background.

If we wanted a bigger night out than what was on offer at the local pubs, it was off to the Marquee or the Speakeasy. The Speak stood out to me because you could actually get a decent steak there. The burgers were also good. In fact, the food was the main reason I went there, even though it was a 'showcase' gig for new record company signings or bands trying to rev up a deal. For the life of me I can't remember one band I ever saw there. I'm not sure what that says about the quality of the bands or my attitude towards them. More likely I would have been too busy chowing down in the restaurant. Thankfully I'm blessed with a metabolism that doesn't let me put on weight. It's a family trait.

You would see some unusual things at the Speakeasy, which was more exclusive than the Marquee. The Marquee was a much more happening place; it was a gig for the punters, which made it the place for us to play. It was real. The Speak, however, was music industry through and through. The typical rock and roll punter would have had more chance getting into Buckingham Palace.

I had some interesting nights at the joint. I was in the restaurant with one of the young ladies from Barnes when Steve Jones and Paul Cook of the Sex Pistols decided to invade our booth. I could understand—my pal from Barnes was smokin' hot—but it soon became evident that she wasn't the main attraction. What was of particular interest was my steak.

'Wotcha, mate, yer not gonna eat all that, are you?' Jones said to me, smacking his lips.

So we shared my meal and I got a round of beer in. Steve was a real character, great company, but I got the impression that he was on the way to becoming a self-parody. As for Paul the drummer, he was trying to be way too cool but at least he left my food alone. He did get my dinner guest a bit offside, though, when he commented: 'Love ya tits, luv.' Still, I'm sure he meant it as a compliment and, in his defence, Sharon did have a spectacular rack.

Brian Robertson and Phil Lynott of the band Thin Lizzy were regulars at the Speakeasy and were regularly very out of it along with a drinking buddy, singer Frankie Miller. Brian had a habit of carrying around a stuffed dog, a kid's cuddly toy, of which he was obsessively protective. I was at the Speak one night when a brawl broke out between Brian and Frankie Miller which left Brian with a severed artery in his hand, and blood pissing everywhere. It caused him to miss a US tour supporting Queen. Rumour had it that the ruckus started when Frankie got hold of Brian's dog and tore its head off.

I got into a few conversations with Phil Lynott but couldn't decipher a word he said, due to his Irish accent and the speed at which he spoke. It was like trying to have a conversation with an auctioneer. Some nights he would be very friendly, and wave or shout out from across the bar, while at other times he would stalk into the club, do a couple of circuits, obviously looking for someone, and walk straight out again without acknowledging a soul.

ϟ

Malcolm never let on that he was ever a Marc Bolan/T Rex fan (I wish I had known that at the time) but I'm sure his eyebrows raised a little when we were booked to make our UK television debut on *Superpop*, a show produced by a guy named Mike Mansfield. We didn't know Mike from a bar of soap but were told he was a big shot. The show, named 'Rollin' Bolan', was filmed at the Wimbledon Theatre on 13 July 1976 and was a comeback special of sorts for Marc Bolan and another 'artist', Leapy Lee. Leapy had a novelty hit called 'Little Arrows' and was also on the comeback trail.

Marc Bolan's appeal was always lost on me. I was surprised how big he had actually been in the UK—massive, in fact—but he had gone missing from the public eye and the charts for one reason or another and this was to be the start of his big comeback.

AC/DC was opening the show. It was a coup for us, a new band, to get national television exposure, and we were very keen to make this one stick. But we felt a fair amount of angst when it became apparent that we had to use the back line amplifiers supplied and not our own gear. Using unfamiliar gear for any gig is fraught with danger but here we had ten minutes to get some sounds together for three songs that we were to play to millions across the UK. It was a serious opportunity and we didn't want to blow it.

With all due respect to those who supplied the gear, which I'm sure was top notch, it wasn't ours, so the guitar sounds were out of whack. You spend years refining your sound, so to be presented with a debut spot on UK TV and not have 'our sound' at our fingertips was a big fucking deal. We sucked it up and got on with it. As Mal's mantra went: 'Hey, you gotta eat shit.'

Consequently the guitar sounds were dodgy compared to the usual Young wall of sound, but we got through it well enough. We opened with 'Livewire', followed by 'Can I Sit Next to You Girl', one of my favourite AC/DC numbers, with a killer (and rare) Mal solo at the front of it. I haven't a clue what the other song was; possibly 'It's a Long Way to the Top'.

As difficult as our UK TV debut was, we did have Marc Bolan to add some perspective to the day. It wasn't often that AC/DC stayed around to watch any other act. Bolan's appearance on stage was funny at the start but the laughs wore off pretty quickly for me. He looked a mess; it didn't help that he was a little, rotund fellow, caked with drag queen make-up, tottering around the stage aimlessly on ridiculously high platform heels. I was waiting for him to go arse-up. I suffered through one completely unrecognisable tune and that was enough. I never got what the fuss was about with Bolan and I saw nothing that day to change my view. He had the look of a guy who was rapidly nearing his use-by date. (Bolan died in a car crash in September 1977.)

We got to watch the TV broadcast of the show at the Red Cow soon after. We were gigging there that night and managed to time it so we could watch our bit in the between-sets break. George Young and Harry Vanda were in town at the time and watched with us. George was very taken with 'Can I Sit Next to You Girl', cheering Malcolm along during his guitar solo. But what did the band think of our UK TV debut? Not much, it was just another TV show. Ho hum.

We had accidentally discovered what would become our London power base, the Marquee, via the two gigs we did supporting Back Street Crawler on 11 and 12 May 1976. We immediately felt at home there: it was small, smoky and decidedly grimy, absolutely perfect for us. It was a lot like the Hard Rock Café, Michael Browning's club in Melbourne, which we'd used as a sort of band clubhouse.

There were a few notable London gigs that would help AC/DC brew up a faithful following: the aforementioned Red Cow in Hammersmith, the Nashville Rooms in West Kensington and the Fulham Greyhound. But the one venue, and crowd, that would really embrace the band was the Marquee. That had a lot to do with Michael Browning and Richard Griffiths spruiking the band to Jack Barrie, the manager of the club. Jack was about the most influential guy in the London scene. After all, this was the man who had been involved with the Marquee since 1965. Jack was also integral to the Reading Festival, another prized gig that we had our eyes on. With Michael and Richard's encouragement, Jack saw one of our Back Street Crawler gigs and picked up on the band. A string of Monday night residencies were set up for August, at the end of the Lock Up Your Daughters jaunt.

These gigs were designed to spread word of mouth on the street, which they did, and quickly. In the London heatwave summer of '76, punk was the flavour of the month and the Sex Pistols were playing just around the corner at the 100 Club on Oxford Street. Regardless, our crowds grew each week. We were starting to cram them into the tiny, smelly club that allegedly had a capacity of 700. There wasn't any air-conditioning so when it was full of the new AC/DC devotees, the atmosphere would turn funky almost instantly; condensation from all the collected sweat would form on the ceiling and rain back onto the punters.

It got so hot in there that on 23 August Angus did the gig without his school uniform. He duck-walked straight onto the Marquee stage in running shoes and a pair of jocks. It was just so fuckin' hot. It was also the reason for me parting with my long hair. I was drenched with sweat even before I started to play and this night I went on in just a pair of jeans and my trusty Doc Martens. A few songs in and it was as if I'd just got out of the shower; my shaggy hair was dripping and slapping all around the place. And headbanging with wet hair has its hazards, as I was about to find out.

While I was playing, a large clump of wet hair went into my mouth. I gagged, spluttered, then swallowed a mass of my own hair. I was on my knees, choking, and going down for the third time, when my trusty roadie and drinking buddy Cod came to my rescue and reefed a solid handful of wet hair out of my throat. Nice spray of blood came with it, too. Fuck that for a joke, I figured; the very next day I was off to see Ben, our hairdresser, to get it all lopped off before it killed me. AC/DC having a hairdresser always makes me chuckle. Coral introduced us to Ben, who worked out of a salon on Kensington High Street.

This run of Mondays did wonders for the band. We created a new attendance record each week, as Jack and his Marquee staff found ways to shoehorn a few extra punters into the sweatbox. The vibe in the club was tailor made for us: hot, sweaty, no bullshit, with carpet that stuck to the soles of your shoes and a sound so fuckin' loud the bottles on the bar vibrated while we played. It was a perfect storm for breeding a new crew of AC/DC headbangers.

The guitarist Ritchie Blackmore was at one of our Marquee gigs. Ritchie had put together his own band called Rainbow, after helping create some of the all-time great hard rock albums with Deep Purple. Ritchie's guitar playing was a main feature of Deep Purple and I suspect that even Angus had a smidgin of respect for the guy, albeit grudgingly. Blackmore, however, was a tad sniffy about us, commenting that we 'had nothing new to offer'.

Perhaps Blackmore was still a bit peeved about the guys and brother George beating up on the Deep Purple crew at the Sunbury Festival back in 1975. Purple had played and by some accounts stunk the place up bad, so they got a little huffy and wouldn't allow AC/DC to set up their gear and play. (I'm quoting from band folklore as it was before I joined.) Anyway, a brawl broke out on stage in full view of the crowd, who cheered the local lads on. While AC/DC didn't get to play at Sunbury, they did get a shitload of publicity for having the balls to take on the superstars' crew. No surprises there.

But who cared about Blackmore when we had Jack Barrie on our side? He had adopted AC/DC, calling us 'the most exciting band to play at the Marquee since Led Zeppelin'. Jack ensured we got a place on the bill at the Reading Festival, which seemed like a great idea at the time. We'd play our last Marquee gig on 8 September, just four months after appearing there as nobodies supporting Back Street Crawler. But it had been a big four months for the band—we'd started off at zero and ended up beating The Who and Jimi Hendrix for the Marquee attendance record. 'This is definitely going to work,' I thought to myself.

The Reading Festival, held in late August 1976, was and still is a big deal for a band trying to make a name for itself in England. It's the country's longest-running music festival. Spread over a few days and several stages, it regularly pulls upwards of 50,000 punters. Michael and Coral Browning and our agent, Richard Griffiths, did some serious lobbying to get us on the bill, and, of course, Jack Barrie's support did wonders.

It's probably the only time I can recall Malcolm being clearly on edge before a show, unlike Angus, who was always jumpy prior to a gig. I think it would be impossible to do what Angus did on stage without getting wound up, particularly when we only had thirty minutes to make an impression. But this gig was different; it had a much different feel to it. I didn't feel comfortable before the show and I wasn't alone.

There were a number of things that set this gig apart. There were the obvious differences: it was a big outdoor show that guaranteed us a heap of exposure, although playing a gig in broad daylight was a novelty for AC/DC. George and Harry had flown in especially for the show, and while it was a pleasure to have them along, their presence certainly upped the tension. They'd checked us out any time they could in Australia, but now in England it was another thing altogether—we were rocking for much higher stakes. They knew that; we knew it too. I had the distinct feeling that they wanted to make their presence felt.

We saw Reading as a super opportunity to boost our visibility and to liven up sales of the UK version of *High Voltage*. Right now it wasn't exactly setting the charts on fire (I still want to know who approved that cover shot, a point I heard Michael raising with Coral). The UK charts were currently full of Elton John, Dr Hook, Wings and the Bee Gees—surely there was a place for us among such lightweight fluff. And we stood out at Reading, too—apart from the blues guitarist Rory Gallagher, there were the prog-rockers Van der Graaf Generator, Manfred Mann's Earth Band and an alleged 'supergroup' named Camel, which included members of Roxy Music. With the exception of Gallagher, these were the type of acts that we fancied we'd be able to blow clear off the stage.

Reading was a short drive from London, out past Ascot, where Richard Griffiths' parents lived. We'd decided on a drop-in en route to the gig. I have no idea what Richard's parents made of us, a scruffy bunch of streetwise Aussies, but I'm sure that there would have been a lot of spadework done to prepare them. It was obvious that Richard came from the upper classes, which made our collective lack of class a source of amusement. His swanky family home reflected his upbringing; there was even a massive croquet lawn out the back. Now, from my experience there are many typical ways for a band on the make to prepare for an important gig, but sandwiches, white wine and a relaxed round of croquet in genteel company doesn't immediately spring to mind. But that's exactly what we did before leaving for Reading.

So off we headed to the gig. It was an unusual set-up at Reading. There was an extra-wide stage that allowed for two independent band set-ups. A band would be playing on one side while up the other end another would be rigging up in plain sight of the punters. No rock and roll mystery here. The stage situation had a strange effect; by playing on one side you were only really connecting with part of the audience, if you were connecting at all. I think we were more suited to this unconventional set-up than some because we had two very mobile front men in Bon and Angus, but it really gave me the feeling of the large crowd being sliced down the middle. And the crowd seemed to be very happy to sit on its collective arse (and their hands) while we were playing.

To call the reaction apathetic would have been complimentary and it was all the more sedate because of the size of the crowd. There is nothing like a huge audience making no noise, no nothing, just sitting there, taking in the all-too-rare English sunshine. I distinctly recall during a break between songs I heard a lone punter yelling, 'Get on with it.' That's how quiet it was, I could pick out a smartarse heckler among 50,000 people.

It was one thing to be playing a small gig to little reaction; we could usually turn that around with a few sparks from Angus, just like that gig where Ahmet Ertegün showed up late. But it's a different story in front of a large crowd, especially when there is zero energy feeding back to you. Our battery was flat and nothing we could do on stage that day gave us a kickstart. Manic American rocker Ted Nugent went on straight after us. He had an album called *Cat Scratch Fever* that was on the verge of breaking and he was getting a heap of press about his thing for hunting with a bow and arrow and basically being the current 'Wild Man of Rock'. It was all excellent PR but from what I saw he suffered much the same reaction from the cool afternoon crowd. Apathy ruled.

Despite our fair share of hype, I had the feeling that the majority of the Reading crowd was seeing us for the first time; they needed to be convinced that all the fuss was warranted. But Reading was a disaster. There was so much riding on this gig, and there were some serious questions asked afterwards. It's one thing for your band to fail at a major festival in front of a huge audience, but to have your record producer and mentor there, who is not only a bit of a firebrand but has his little brothers in the band, well, throw in some alcohol and a shitfight was set to erupt.

Things were indeed a tad icy after the show. We knew we'd blown a big opportunity. I had what I now recognise as a bad habit of bailing out of the band room quickly after a dud show, when I should have hung about for a post-mortem and not made myself such an easy target. (Isn't hindsight wonderful?) A band on the road is a very political beast—a detractor one day can be your greatest ally the next, so the verdict would usually get back to me via the band grapevine. Still, a word of advice to young rockers everywhere: if you value your position in a band, don't be in a rush to get out of the band room if a gig goes pear-shaped. Stick around until someone else bails to get a beer or chase a girl.

It was decided all of us, sans Bon, would go back to the band house and have a game of cards and some beers. By the time we returned to HQ the finger-pointing had begun, and many of those digits were aimed in my direction. We'd started to play a game of nine-card brag, when the Reading gig came up in conversation. Malcolm, George and Angus got particularly animated while Phil, wisely, kept out of the firing line. Bar Angus, of course, we'd all had a few by then but certainly weren't out of control. George looked at me and asked what I was thinking towards the end of the show—why did I look so surly? I remember this very clearly. I said I was getting frustrated at the reaction of the crowd.

As dumb answers go, this was a doozy.

I'd seen George blow up at his brothers before and also give Bon a bit of a tune-up, but this was a first for yours truly. He lit into me.

'You were pissed off? Well, it fuckin' showed too! Who do you think you fuckin' are, anyway?'

He continued his tirade, while his fellow Youngs looked on and said nothing. I got the distinct feeling that my future with the band had already been discussed. I was getting worked up too, and would have been happy to go on with it, but the fact was George was one hundred per cent right. He felt that I had given less than was required and I really had no comeback. But what I objected to was the way his criticism was being delivered.

Things started to get even messier after that, so much so that Angus went upstairs to his bedroom, followed closely by George, still giving him a loud rundown of the situation as he saw it. The rest of us kept on playing cards until Mal went upstairs to calm things down. He didn't stand a chance; now it was on for young and old. It was a full-on brawl, the only three-way blue I have ever seen—and between brothers, no less. By the time I got upstairs to try to break things up Mal had lost a few clumps of hair and punches were flying everywhere. Instinctively, I grabbed George—and whack!

'Get your fuckin' hands off him!'

Now I was getting belted. Thank Christ they were only little guys who couldn't really hurt you or I would have been in serious trouble. There's a lesson to be learned here: never try to break up a fight between brothers, especially when there's three of them. After things calmed down we got back to the game of cards. Eventually, I got the chance to ask Ian, a friend of the Youngs who was visiting at the time, why he didn't come upstairs to help out.

'Get fucked,' he said. 'I've seen it all before.'

Up until this time I'd never felt the need to watch my back but in the coming days messages started making their way back to me. My particular favourite was: 'Who does he think he is? Jack fuckin' Bruce?'

Jack Bruce was the virtuoso bass player from British supergroup Cream, and I certainly wasn't him, and I'm still not now, but it really pissed me off to have my commitment to the band questioned. It struck home hard because of the Reading gig. Unfortunately, this was the start of my real problems within AC/DC.

Not long after the Reading disaster, in late September 1976, we were in Hamburg, Germany, starting our first European tour, supporting Ritchie Blackmore's new band Rainbow. Blackmore had evidently got over the fact that he thought we had nothing to offer and agreed to have AC/DC on the bill. What I think helped was the £10,000 'buy on' fee that was paid to secure the tour spot for us—and there he was thinking we had nothing to offer. What a silly sausage.

Hamburg. Now there's a town where a band like us could really get up to some mischief. Alex Young, the fourth Young brother, was our tour guide. Alex was a musician, sax player and part-time bassist who was in the band Grapefruit, one of the first signings to Apple, the Beatles' record label. Alex introduced us to the Reeperbahn, the red-light strip of Hamburg—and, as I found out, there was no red light brighter than Hamburg's.

One place of particular interest was the Eros Center. It was like a multi-storey car park but rather than cars it was filled with hookers. While in Hamburg do as the Hamburgers do, so we all felt it was right to explore the endless possibilities of the Eros Center. What the process entailed was locating your particular taste/fetish/peccadillo, have a chat, negotiate the price and upstairs you went to a room to seal the deal, so to speak. And how do I know so much? One of the other guys told me. Honest.

The real buzz of the place was the choice: the girls came in all shapes and sizes, from tiny to massive. And I mean big, maybe the best part of 120–130 kilos. All fantasies were catered for, too: there were nurses, maids, straight-looking secretarial types, biker girls, identical twins, women dressed as guys, grannies. Some even looked like hookers! One girl was kitted out in full circus clown gear. I'm a liberal-thinking kind of guy, but that was too weird for me.

We used a bar on the Reeperbahn, owned by a pal of Alex's, as a rendezvous point. There was plenty of coming and going on. We would refresh ourselves with steins of (thankfully) cold beer, shots of schnapps and even food, sometimes. Hamburg is just that kind of town.

We spent one night out on the town with Earl McGrath, one of the top guys from Atlantic Records. Earl was on his way to becoming president of Rolling Stones Records on the recommendation of Ahmet Ertegün, and he seemed to know his way around Hamburg. One night we ended up in a club late at night hitting the turps hard (Earl was picking up the tab) and he told us to keep an eye on the table in front of us.

Lights dimmed, some moody music started up and a guy draped himself over the table and was joined by possibly the hottest, most stacked woman I had ever seen. Did I mention they were both nude? Then the table started rotating and rising slowly so everyone in the club could get a good look at the proceedings. What was becoming very apparent was this guy had what appeared to be a third leg. Seriously, this guy's dick had to be eighteen inches long and the bastard looked fairly pleased with himself. It all got a bit messy after that; I'm glad we were out of range.

The Rainbow tour took us through what was then West Germany, including Hamburg, Bremen, Cologne, Nuremburg and Munich—just in time for Oktoberfest. Mal, Phil and I got into the Oktoberfest mood, buying the silly hats and cigars that were the necessary gear while visiting the numerous beer halls. The pick was the Löwenbräu Keller, a massive joint that held a few thousand people and in which the very cold beer was dispensed in litre steins that were a real handful to down, especially when you were nursing a foot-long cigar.

Up on the raised stage in the centre of the Löwenbräu was the obligatory oom-pah-pah band, churning out non-stop polkas while clad in funny hats and lederhosen that were being seriously stress-tested by some more than ample German rear ends. On the half hour a group of prancing Germans (more lederhosen) would appear on stage, go into a routine of more prancing and giving each other a solid slap around the chops with a bit of yodelling thrown in. On the hour the band would break into a polka version of 'Waltzing Matilda' and the Aussies in the crowd (sans lederhosen) would just slap each other around.

Mal, Phil and I drank and polka'd deep into the Oktoberfest night and got absolutely shit-faced. We awoke the next day with headaches that would have killed an elephant, but we weren't sure if it was the beer, cigars, the oom-pah-pah band or the cumulative effect of all three that made us feel like we were not long for this earth. There was only one way out: stock up on silly hats and cigars and get straight back to the Löwenbräu Keller to polka up another storm.

We escaped Munich and the Oktoberfest (just) to continue with the Rainbow tour. I started to hit the wonderful German beer hard and had, for a change of pace, taken a liking to shots of schnapps in between the giant steins of Löwenbräu. I should have seen the writing on the wall from past experience—whenever I hit the turps athletically it was either out of boredom or just plain unhappiness. On the Rainbow tour, well, put me down for both. There were the lighter moments, great times, like the Oktoberfest jaunts with Mal and Phil, but the whole treadmill—do the show, try to sleep, drive 400 kilometres to the next town, eat some crap, do the next show, try to sleep again—was fucking me up.

I was using the booze as a blanket and learned that by drinking more I could keep a hangover at bay. I lived for those thirty minutes or so on stage; that was the fix. The band was on fire but the other twenty-three and a half hours of each day was a giant pain in the arse. It was mind-numbing. I have never been one to get stoned out of my brain and switch off, but the problem was that if you didn't switch off, well, you went nuts.

I had never considered a life without AC/DC, but with the tension of being relegated to a support band and catching a large amount of the associated crap that comes with that, I started to sense all was not well with me and the band. It was like the old story about a poker game: if you can't work out who the sucker is after the first few hands, well, it's probably you. And the mere thought that my spot in the band might be under threat made my guts churn. It wasn't rare for me to be ripping along an autobahn, riding shotgun with Phil at the wheel, nodding off thinking: 'I really don't give a fuck if I don't wake up.' The feeling was that intense.

While still in Germany I had my first close encounter with the type of depression that too much time on the road can bring on. Bon could be a very lonely guy at times and I came to understand how that felt. It's weird: you can be on the road with a couple of bands, twenty crew and assorted hangers on, playing to full houses every night, and still be lonely. I think it's the isolation that does it—and those damned hotel rooms. You can be in the best hotel in the world and feel like shit, or stay in a dump and have one of the biggest nights of your life. Weird.

I can still recall the resignation I felt this particular night in Dortmund. I was in a hotel room many floors up and it occurred to me that it would be very easy to just open the window and jump. It appealed to me at that moment; it was compelling. I have to tell you that right then it made sense. I had made the conscious decision, without thought for the consequences and the damage that would be left behind. All I felt was sheer relief: 'Here's a way out'—straight through a window. I wasn't pissed, I'd just had enough. Even thinking about it now is very unsettling; it was a close call. For ages I tried to get the window open, while some German newsreader was gabbing away on the TV. It's not something you can call the concierge about, really.

'Suite 746 here, can you come up and open the window, please? I want to top myself and I can't seem to get the damned thing open.'

Life for me at that weird moment made less sense than the German newsreader. I guess depression had kicked in; the road will do that. It's a fact of the road that no matter how thrilling it can be playing big shows, travelling the world and sampling the local talent, you'll reach a point where you're as lonely as fuck and alone in a hotel somewhere—you don't even know what town you are in. When I gave myself over to a cause like AC/DC it didn't just rule my life, *it was my life*. For all intents and purposes I was no longer in control; I didn't have the luxury to pull a sickie and go fishing, or sleep in another hour and go in to work late. What was demanded in AC/DC was 1000 per cent commitment. I had no issue with that but if you are not cut out for it, it will eat you up, and in Dortmund it was chowing down on me, big time. And I had none of the outlets that guys do on the road these days—international phone calls were rare because of the cost. I do envy the guys touring these days—email, Skype, watching your local footy team play live on the net . . . luxury!

Fortunately the feeling passed, but it's an unearthly thing to experience. I understand how people decide to take that path; they just reach the end of the line and can't make sense of existence. I'm not saying it's right, of course it isn't, it's the ultimate act of selfishness, but it's depression, pure and simple. Thankfully those real black days are behind me, although I'm not completely immune to bouts of depression. It now just seems very normal to have occasional off days. I realise that Bon was prone to depression, too. I wish I had been more tuned into the feeling at the time. But it just wasn't in my 'get laid, get pissed, get laid again' rock musician's handbook.

The Rainbow tour took us further south and introduced AC/DC to new markets: France, Holland, Belgium and Switzerland. We were going over very well indeed, considering the punters were all there for Blackmore and had little or no idea who the fuck we were or why the guitar player was wearing a school uniform. *Was ist das?* But I think AC/DC's no-bullshit rock and roll stacked up impressively against Blackmore's overblown, leaning towards the mystical, fifteen- to twenty-minute epics. Ritchie Blackmore is an all-time great guitar player, without question, but the show just went on and on.

What didn't help momentum was a fifteen-minute keyboard solo and a drum solo of similar length. The saving grace? The drummer was Cozy Powell. If you had to endure a drum solo you wanted him in the seat.

We all agreed the best part of the show was when they cranked up the Deep Purple classic 'Mistreated'. It truly ripped and the vocalist Ronnie James Dio was born to sing it. It was astounding that this massive, operatic voice could emanate from such a tiny frame. We buddied up with Ronnie very early on; in fact, he made a point of chasing down Mal and Angus, introducing himself and telling the story of how his band the Electric Elves supported big brother George and the Easybeats on some US dates.

A feature of Rainbow's stage setting was an electronic rainbow—funny that—which straddled the stage and was programmed for some 'stunning lighting effects', or so everyone was promised. What became a highlight of the tour was said rainbow coughing, spluttering and generally malfunctioning. It had a mind of its own and Blackmore was apt to get into a real foot-stomping tizz when his rainbow was out of sorts. This became a regular feature, something we all looked forward to. I was waiting for Blackmore to hold his breath and turn blue, because his rainbow sure wasn't.

He also insisted on nothing but candlelight in his private dressing room. Maybe he was on some medieval kick, who knows, but the candles had to be lit ready for his arrival. Cod, our stage roadie, could always get a Blackmore tizz going by sneaking in and blowing the candles out.

'I want to know who is blowing my candles out NOW and bring them here NOW!' announced the star of the show. We didn't say a word.

There was a notice posted in the backstage area warning that anyone caught blowing out Ritchie's candles 'will be dismissed immediately'. Oh, fuck off!

Our first European tour was an interesting experience and it confirmed our suspicion that the so-called 'big' names were not worth losing sleep over. I figured we just had to keep gigging, touring, plugging away, getting the Bon and Angus show to the punters, and then it was only a question of time.

ϟ

By late October '76 we were back in London and gearing up for our next UK tour, a sixteen-date jaunt taking in some of the major cities that were beginning to warm to us, including Birmingham, Liverpool, Newcastle and, of course, Glasgow, our new spiritual home, as well as its near neighbour Edinburgh, and London.

While there was a whiff of familiarity about the tour, I could sense a vibe building on the band. There were more punters and their behaviour was increasingly feral. The band's following was starting to morph into a mass of long-haired, denim-clad, patch-wearing males, with very few females in sight—although there were a few stand-outs that made themselves known to us from time to time. The male-dominated crowd was just what Michael Browning had envisaged, his theory being that the guys would become long-time fans and stick with the band, whereas female punters were thought to be a lot more fickle. Radio airplay and TV exposure was still thin on the ground for AC/DC, we weren't selling many albums, so it was AC/DC business as usual—get out there and gig, gig, gig.

We were starting to pull respectable numbers outside of London purely through word of mouth. Glasgow City Hall on 2 November was a rowdy, raucous gig; the Glaswegians made it plain that they were taking ownership of the band—they weren't adopting us, we were home already. This was only our second gig in the Youngs' hometown but there was a real warmth to the crowd. Don't get me wrong, it wasn't a love-in, it was something else, more like a party with a load of good mates. It was becoming apparent to me that there was an identifiable sound to a Scots crowd, a sound unlike any other. It was more intense, louder. Maybe it was the Glenfiddich working its wonders.

Even leaving the gig was different; there were a load of guys waiting for us to emerge. As we came through the door cheers broke out, followed by much backslapping and some unintelligible compliments (I think they were compliments) in broad Glaswegian accents. There was a bit of interest in Angus; some of the crowd asked: 'Where's the wee man?' It was all very matey and it provided some welcome warmth because I can tell you it gets fuckin' freezing on a late autumn night in Glasgow.

The tour gradually built to the London date, 10 November at the Hammersmith Odeon. This was the band's first major London gig; sure, we'd built the Marquee dates up to record-breaking proportions, but the bad taste of stiffing at Reading was still in our mouths and a big night at Hammersmith would help wash that away. It wasn't lost on us that little more than six months earlier we were playing our first set in London to a half-empty Red Cow, barely a few hundred metres down the road. Now we were headlining the Hammersmith Odeon. While that was some rapid progress it said plenty about the band's mentality that it was business as usual, no big deal, no big build-up, let's just do it. Sure, there may have been a few more jitters than normal but that was largely due to the mercurial and strangely absent Bon Scott.

After a late-afternoon sound check, we headed back to the hotel, freshened up, got something to eat, and downed a quiet one or two in the hotel bar. Bon was at home with Silver at the Hippie Haven on Gloucester Road, or so we figured. We finished our drinks and headed off to the gig, following our usual practice of arriving an hour before show time. During that hour we'd get ourselves together, check our gear, focus and . . . hey, where's Bon?

'Anyone seen Bon?'

We were tuning up, Angus had the school uniform on, ciggies were lit and the clock was ticking down the final thirty minutes to show time. My mind went back to the Bon Scott no-show at the Hard Rock Café in the early days; it couldn't happen again, could it? Ten minutes before we went on, still no Bon. Michael Browning, who was getting shitty, sent out a search party. There was a palpable tension in the band room; maybe there was something wrong.

'Where the fuck is Bon? We're supposed to be on stage *now*.'

It was starting to become a real big issue when there was some shouting and some laughing.

'Where the fuck have you been, you fuckin' prick!' I heard someone say, very relieved.

An extremely late Bon Scott made his entrance, bag slung over his leather-jacketed shoulder, no apologies, just that big shifty grin on his mug.

It's our first major show in London, so did Bon use a limo to get to the gig?

'Nah,' he replied.

'A taxi?'

'Nah.'

Bon had decided to remain extra low-key and catch the tube for the few stops from Gloucester Road to Hammersmith. No pop-star shit for our Bon. All well and good, but only if he'd got on the right train. Bon, in his own inimitable fashion, had caught a train heading east into the city and was fifteen kilometres from Hammersmith before he twigged to it. Seriously, who the fuck catches a train—the wrong fuckin' train no less—to his first headlining gig at the Hammersmith Odeon? Bon Scott, that's who.

'C'mon, arsehole, we were on twenty minutes ago.'

That was the scene backstage before we walked on stage at the Hammersmith Odeon. Once settled and plugged in, I started off with the bass intro to 'Livewire', while Mal's guitar creeped around. I looked over at Angus, who was stalking the stage from side to side, wound up tight. Then he was up on the drum riser. Just before Angus and Phil kicked it in, Angus took off his cap and slammed onto the stage, raising his arms and growling at the punters. And then—boom, his Gibson SG and Phil's drums hit it. I felt like I was three metres up off the stage; it was the same type of lift-off that scared the crap out of our agent, Richard Griffiths, at the Red Cow show. A lot sure can happen in a space of a few hundred metres.

The rest of the gig was a bit of a blur. We went through all the usual stuff, I know Angus dropped his daks and we finished with 'Baby Please Don't Go'. But the gig just whistled by;

it was so intense that it felt like we were on stage for about fifteen minutes, or at least from where I was standing, anyway.

This was how Tony Stewart from *NME* read the gig: 'The schoolboy brat up on the rostrum smirks maliciously as his opening power chord painfully rattles through our bonces and makes the unnecessary triumphant gesture of wildly tossing his cap to the floor, as if to say: "This is our day!" The day, gawd 'elp us all, AC/DC conquered London.'

Michael Browning had commissioned a photographer to shoot all the action and expressly asked him to get a shot of the front of the Hammersmith Odeon, with AC/DC up in lights. It was a bit squeaky, but what the hell, it was our first time. Among the shots was a snap of Bon strolling leisurely up the front steps of the theatre, bag slung over his shoulder, ready for yet another day at the office. The silly fucker.

Chapter 9

A giant dose

It was bitterly cold in London in late November 1976, particularly for a thin-blooded bloke like me. So I was very pleased to be heading back to Australia for summer. The idea of blue skies, beaches, cold beer and barbecues was a whole lot more inviting than a drab London winter. We were going back to tour and put some much needed funds back into the AC/DC coffers. We'd also record our next album. So this was no cushy holiday back home, if in fact Australia was still AC/DC's home.

We'd broken a lot of new ground in the UK and Europe during 1976 and while I would always consider Australia home there had been a real shift in how the band viewed Oz. It was implicit that the future of AC/DC had little to do with Australia. We hadn't even scratched the surface in the US yet. All that said, the general vibe was that getting back to Australia was a good thing, a chance to spend the holidays with family and friends and take a short break, recharge and get back into Alberts with George and Harry.

We landed in Sydney on 26 November, a Friday. The band and crew checked into the Kingsgate Hyatt in Kings Cross, 200 metres from the Hampton Court Hotel where, in early 1974, AC/DC used to play to US servicemen on R&R from Vietnam. The main attraction at the Kingsgate that night was to be found in Bon's suite. He'd purchased a twenty-five-year-old bottle of Chivas Regal duty free, dressed up in a fancy red velvet pouch. I got the call from Bon that the bottle was about to be opened—would I like a taste? I was there in a heartbeat.

Bon disrobed the Scotch from the red velvet, took a long, loving look and summarily pronounced, 'Fuck it, let's drink her,' and opened the bottle. We sat down in front of a massive window, high up over the city of Sydney. The view was impressive but I was more interested in the Chivas. One taste led to another, as they often do, and it became evident that we were settling in. We sat, drinking the Chivas and having a chat. It was obvious that Bon was already missing Silver. He hadn't been away for forty-eight hours and was talking about her almost non-stop.

The plan was for Silver to meet up with Bon in Sydney early in the New Year. For a guy who had women on tap if he so desired, he was totally devoted to Silver. Being a young bloke still shy of twenty-one, I just didn't get it. His devotion didn't make any sense at all, especially with what was sure to be on offer in the coming months. It's possible that Bon was over his womanising days. I got the impression that he was hankering to settle down with Silver, as much as the demands of AC/DC would allow. After all, AC/DC came first, to the exclusion of everything and everybody else.

The booze was hitting home, especially after spending the last day and a half on a plane from London, but a couple of things weren't adding up for me. This devotion of Bon's was a totally alien concept and Silver certainly didn't give the impression that she was ready for long-term domestic bliss—with Bon or with anyone else. I didn't know her that well, but from what I saw she simply wasn't all 'hearts and flowers' like Bon.

Bon being Bon, he had fallen like a ton of bricks, like he had for Judy King in Melbourne early 1975, much to his detriment. That relationship almost killed him. I thought that Bon would snap out of it; I figured it was either the Scotch or the jet lag talking, or both. If I'd had a more mature outlook I would have realised that it was neither. Bon was looking for something else outside the band and he thought he'd found it in Silver.

Mal and Angus were back at Burwood, catching up with family after seven months away. Their catching up had to be very swift as we were all due back at the airport Saturday morning bound for Melbourne to appear on *Countdown*. That's what the band demanded. Haven't seen your folks for ages? No worries, go see 'em, but make it quick! It was surreal, flying into Melbourne, driving over to the ABC TV studios, going right past the Prahran Hilton but not even having the time to drop in. That's showbiz. There'd be time to catch up once AC/DC business was attended to.

The Australian tour was going to be called 'The Little Cunts Have Done It'—the promoter's idea—but it got boned for the much less offensive 'Giant Dose of Rock 'n' Roll'. As it turned out, we needn't have bothered—some people were determined to find us offensive anyway.

First order of business was do the standard equipment check, so the whole back line of Marshall guitar and bass amps were set up in Armstrong's Studios in South Melbourne. We ran through a few songs to get the cobwebs out and test the gear in preparation for the tour opener at the Myer Music Bowl. A little diversion had been planned for that evening after the gear check. I'm not sure whose idea it was but my guess it was Mal and Angus plotting away. We were going to play an unannounced set at a Richmond pub called the Royal Oak, which ran a gig called the Tiger Lounge, in honour of the Richmond Tigers, the local footie team. I was under the impression that it was going to be a short, low-key warm-up but I either had it wrong or the plans changed. By the time I got to the pub it took thirty minutes to make it into the kitchen, which we were using as a backstage area. For an unannounced gig it sure looked like someone had been doing some announcing. The joint was packed.

We got up and played a half-dozen songs, all old favourites: 'Roll Over Beethoven', 'Jailhouse Rock', 'Whole Lotta Shakin' Goin' On' and others, straight-down-the-line rockers that were cheered on by the punters who were packed in like sardines. It felt really good to be back and the gig set us up nicely for the next night's show.

The Myer Music Bowl was the perfect place to kick off our return to Oz. It's an outdoor amphitheatre in Melbourne's Domain parklands, right on the city's edge, a stone's throw from our old haunt the Hard Rock Café. The 5000-capacity show was a sellout. Only ticket holders were allowed within the gig area, which was enclosed with cyclone-wire fencing. From my viewpoint, it seemed that just as many, if not more, punters had set up outside the fence, enjoying the summer evening, eskies full of beer and a free AC/DC concert about to begin. Even if we looked like ants from way back up on the hill, we were going to make damned sure they could hear us.

We were all dead keen to play again. We were a band that thrived on live gigs and the three-week lay-off between our last UK show and the Music Bowl was more than enough to get us twitchy. Sure, we'd flown halfway around the world, got back home (except for Bon, who was from Western Australia) for some rest and recreation, and caught up with family and friends, but it was now time to strap the guns on and get back into it. Playing live is what we did; if we didn't, well, the world might as well stop spinning.

The gig was a cracker, the reaction was great, the punters were kicking arse but what was really noticeable was the sound generated by the crowd. I'd forgotten the ear-piercing sound of young chicks screaming; I'd become more used to hearing a mostly male reaction, like the crowds in Glasgow that sounded more like a footy crowd than what I was hearing at the Music Bowl. There were some blokes in the crowd too, but not down the front. The guys that resembled our UK following were on the other side of the fence getting shit-faced. Just who were our fans here in Australia? The divide had widened, or so it seemed to us. It looked like we still had a fan hangover from the *Countdown*/satin jacket days; you'd have thought the teen screamers had moved on. But so what? Scream your hearts out, girls! And they did.

The gig was an outstanding success and seemed like the ideal start to a tour that would take us to all the major cities and states of Australia. It was summer, the weather was bound to be great, the beer cold, and if all the gigs went down like this one, it was all looking good. Too good.

Momentum is a funny thing. When you're flying, not

putting a foot wrong, success breeds confidence and that brings more success. It takes a lot to stop momentum like that, or a lot of little things, at least. And it was a little thing that started to bring things undone. In our case—my case, to be precise—it was the tour program.

The promoters had whipped up this glossy number, very well put together, something for the punters to buy at the gig. The program included individual shots of all the band members on stage with a 'quotable quote' at the top of each photo. The aforementioned young screamers would be dropped off at our gig, scream their lungs out, buy a program, then get picked up by Mum and/or Dad.

'How was the show, dear?'

'Great, I bought a program.'

All well and good, until little Sharon or Sharleen's parents got to page eight. There was a shot of me, accompanied by the caption: 'I'd like to make enough money so I could fuck Britt Ekland.' For the record I would have loved to make enough money to be playing in Rod Stewart's league. But what was to come was the opening shower of a shitstorm that would stink us up for the rest of the tour.

Now that the program was out there, there were loads of complaints, calls to talkback radio, all kinds of crap. It got to the point that we had to withdraw the program from sale under the threat of obscenity charges. Just who was going to be charged was never made clear, but thanks for putting those words on my page, guys—it wasn't even my quote. It was, in fact, a Bon Scott special.

One morning, I was making my way to my regular seat down the back of the tour bus, when Bon motioned to me and patted the seat next to him.

'Sit down, mate,' he said. 'I've a little bit of friendly advice for you.'

'Shit,' I thought, 'what's going on?' This was looking serious; something was clearly troubling Bon.

'Listen, Mark, you really shouldn't be saying such awful things about Britt Ekland. The girl's got feelings, you know.' Bon then went back to his comic book, a huge smirk on his dial.

ϟ

The next hiccup followed close on the heels of the program debacle. Angus had been doing his striptease number and baring his skinny butt at gigs for some time. It caused a bit of a stir but it was all in fun. It was very tongue in, erm, cheek. But trouble started brewing when we arrived for a press conference. The photographers wanted a group shot, so we lined up and Angus dropped trou', bared his arse and put his cap on his bare butt. There was a gasp from a female in the room. She announced that Angus was 'disgusting'.

'My arse is better-looking than my face,' he replied, which got some laughs.

It was no big deal, or so we thought. But from then on Angus's bare arse seemed to attract a whole lot of attention. Bon was even moved to make a comment in *RAM* magazine. 'You see his backside in the papers more than you see his face, which is preferable as far as I'm concerned.'

We started to work our way north, through Shepparton and on to Albury, on the New South Wales side of the border. This time it was the town clerk of Albury who started throwing the shit around. He basically warned us to 'change our tune' if we wanted to play in Albury again. Had he even seen the gig? No, of course not—but he had read about it. A pattern quickly developed: local officials read what dirty little fuckers we were supposed to be and objected to us without having any real idea what they were objecting to. Well, okay, they were offended by Angus's spotty behind. I too found his arse objectionable to look at—and I was in close range—but I took it in the light in which it was intended. It was a lark. This was a rock show, for fuck's sake, not a church service.

Local police started to give us pre-show warnings. 'Any arse-baring and that's it, the power's going to be cut. The gig'll be over and you'll be slapped with obscenity charges.' There were plenty of small-town pen-pushers getting their name in the papers simply by calling us 'disgusting'. It was really getting out of hand when some clown from Wagga Wagga announced that we weren't welcome in his town—and we weren't even scheduled to play there. The mayor of Tamworth banned us from playing in the 'home of country music'. It was becoming ridiculous, especially so if you'd ever seen Angus's arse.

News crews started to fly in from Sydney to cover the 'big story'. They probably passed me in the air, as I had to fly to Sydney to get a 'giant dose' treated by a doctor. It wouldn't have been too wise to get a local quack to treat me. It was all getting very silly now. The general mood on the tour bus was, 'Who needs this shit?'

The major pop/rock radio station was Sydney's 2SM, who'd been instrumental in pushing AC/DC back in 1975, along with Melbourne's 3XY and *Countdown*. But now 2SM turned against us; they banned us from airplay and even refused to accept any advertising promoting our shows. Their general manager came up with this ripper: 'Members of Australian punk rock group AC/DC must decide if they are strippers or musicians. Until they do, the station will not associate with them in any way.' What the fuck was all the shit about?

We hit the coast of Queensland and we were heading south to the Pink Poodle, our favourite hotel on the Gold Coast. The people running the hotel were cool, always welcoming, friendly and unbelievably tolerant of our late-night shenanigans. It was a pleasant change to check into a hotel and get a smile, rather than the usual 'we don't care for any of your carrying-on here'. Phil and I sat down to dinner that night in the restaurant when one of the owners, a lovely lady in her mid-forties, approached us.

'Dinner is on us tonight,' she said. 'You boys have been having a rough trot.'

Phil and I smiled at her; it was a lovely gesture after all the crap we'd been enduring.

Then Phil piped up: 'Any chance you could have a chat to the mayor of Tamworth for us?'

ϟ

We were tough enough to deal with what was being thrown our way, but it did make us question our return. Why bother if we had to deal with all this petty stupidity? At best, I think 'bemused' would have been a fitting description of the band's attitude. AC/DC was, and still is, all about playing to the punters who cared enough to show up and buy a ticket—even if they couldn't buy a program.

After playing the Miami High School Great Hall—can't remember anything that great about it—on 23 December we split up for Christmas and the New Year. Phil and I flew to Melbourne to check in with our families, while Mal and Angus headed to Sydney, with Bon in tow.

Yet throughout December 1976 we were on the receiving end of some interesting press. Ian McDougall reported in Melbourne's *Truth*—hardly the *Washington Post*—the travails of a wealthy Double Bay dowager. The story ran under the headline POP HIT MAKES WIDOW'S PHONE RUN HOT. An AC/DC fan had started calling the number 36-24-36, which Bon spelled out in 'Dirty Deeds Done Cheap' ('call me anytime, I lead a life of crime'). The put-upon Double Bay matron was threatening all kinds of legal action; her lawyers had contacted Alberts and she was demanding that the record and all printed music be withdrawn from sale, just like our recently deceased program.

The bit I did like in the story was this: 'Scores of AC/DC fans telephoned her requesting details of the hit record. Others were less polite and made crude suggestions.' Not AC/DC fans, surely! It was reported that she suffered 'abuse, ridicule and obscene calls'. Chris Gilbey from Alberts called her to apologise officially and profusely. He found the harassed widow a new phone number, and even had cards printed that she could hand out to her cronies.

'It has caused the woman and our company some anxious moments and we can't apologise enough for the stress she went through,' Chris told the paper, duly chastened. Nice one, Chris.

Another story that went nationwide referred to a couple of schoolgirls from Peakhurst, in Sydney's south, who wagged school to greet us at Sydney Airport. This particular headline screamed UPROAR ON GIRL TATTOOS and quoted a fifteen-year-old girl: 'If my mother ever found out,' she admitted, 'she would kill me.' Not the smartest thing you could share with a reporter. The journo described the tattoos in question: 'One will say AC/DC and the other will feature a bluebird . . . the name Malcolm, the band's leader/guitarist, will feature under the bluebird.' See the problem here? There were no actual tattoos to speak of; our schoolgirl fan was saying that she *wanted* to get some ink done.

'I love them all and when I save up enough money I'm going to have tattoos done on my body,' she added, which was perhaps a little more damning.

One girl from Bondi (no age given) proudly showed the reporter the crude tattoo she had inscribed on her arm. 'I had it done because Bon, the singer, has them.' The article ended with this choice slice of investigative journalism. 'The band underwent an hour and a quarter search by customs officers before they were cleared.' Really? That was news to all of us. Didn't happen.

Our Giant Dose of Rock 'n' Roll homecoming, that had started so well at the Myer Music Bowl, was heading straight down the crapper. 'What the fuck, Merry Christmas,' was all I could come up with as I flew back to Melbourne.

ϟ

There's no place like home at Christmas, even if home was the Prahran Hilton. My mother and her partner Joe Loughrey were living at the Hilton, in part because Joe was the caretaker of 1 Surrey Road, South Yarra, but to be honest, they liked it there. I did note that the old place had settled down somewhat in my absence. The locals seemed a lot less restless, but that may have been the Yuletide spirit. It was good to be surrounded by family, catch up and deal out a few pressies that I had picked up for my crew. It was the season to be jolly, after all.

Having arrived home on Christmas Eve, my plan was to kick back, put my feet up after a very solid twenty months (for me at least, more for the rest of the guys) and enjoy the break. Anyway, that was the plan. But I found it impossible to unwind. I was wired, completely incapable of relaxing; my wheels were spinning. What was troubling me the most was that I didn't feel at home, even though that's exactly where I was. The worst part of the day was when 8.30 or 9 pm rolled around, what would normally be gig time. I would get this sense of expectation that something was about to happen, and then anxiety kicked in when it didn't.

The answer was to round up my pal Graham Kennedy and hit the town, hard. The Station Hotel (what a surprise) and the other local pubs got a good run; I also went along to see Graham's gigs. I was riding shotgun for him, which was a pleasant change. There was just no way I could stay in at night. What started as a breather turned into a serious bender, and soon enough I was getting absolutely ploughed every night, big time. I would wake up each day around lunchtime, freshen up and walk the 200 metres to the local pub, the Court Jester on Chapel Street, Prahran, for a counter lunch and a few settling ales. The next course consisted of Scotch and Cokes. I would get back to the Hilton late afternoon, sleep off the booze, have dinner with Mum and Joe and then hit the town again with Graham.

As Graham and I kicked back in the front bar at the Station Hotel with a cold beer and a Scotch, I took the chance to reflect on my recent past. A lot had happened in the last year and a half. I was sitting a couple of steps away from the spot where I was smashed in the face with a beer jug and then came to on the footpath outside, coughing up blood. And it was where my AC/DC journey started, despite almost getting derailed by the Station Hotel's owners, Albert and Marino. When I joined, the band was on the bare bones of its arse, to the point where Phil had to buy dowel from the local hardware because he couldn't afford proper drumsticks. Now we'd just headlined at London's Hammersmith Odeon and opened our homecoming tour to a sold-out Myer Music Bowl.

What had changed? And had I changed? Not much, apparently, because here I was, back at the Station front bar, getting plastered again. Still. Yeah, not much, if you discounted playing hundreds of gigs in Australia, the UK, Europe and Scandinavia, having one of the top-selling Oz albums of 1976 and earning enough dough to splash out on Chrissie presents for family and friends. And there was the prospect of a shitload more gigs to come, all over the world. Was I happy? I wasn't sure. I needed a round to think that one over. Thirsty, Graham?

'Another round, boys?' asked Albert from behind the bar. 'I remember AC/DC playing here before you went to England,' he added. 'Great band, the best ever here. These are on the house.'

My stocks must have risen if I was downing free booze at the Station Hotel.

'Might take it easy on the Scotch, I don't want to get pissed,' I said to Albert. 'You might throw me out.' I just couldn't resist.

'Throw *you* out of the Station?' Albert replied, doing a fair impersonation of someone who was genuinely shocked. 'No way, Mark.'

Yep, things had changed.

I was now drinking at least a bottle of Scotch a day, some days closer to two. But the interesting thing was that I wasn't falling-down drunk like most of the people around me; I was always the last man standing. A couple of all-nighters morphed into the next night's festivities. I need to say it was all alcohol-driven, too, absolutely no drugs. My metabolism was flying, doing double duty. I was troubled and the only thing that kept me going was nervous energy. Something kept gnawing away at me. 'If this isn't my home, just where the fuck is it?' The answer I came up with was this: I was at home on the road with the guys; that's where I was truly me. I wasn't the same guy that used to live at the Hilton. I was feeling guilty about not feeling at home there, as if I was being disrespectful.

I was at the Court Jester when a local overheard me saying how much I enjoyed London.

'This place not good enough for you now, eh?' he snapped. Good question.

I gradually came to terms with being unsettled. I realised that I would be back on the road soon enough and that I'd better enjoy my time with my family. Who the fuck knew when I'd next be back? With this straight in my head, my drinking calmed down and I spent an almost alcohol-free New Year's Eve at the Chevron Hotel with my sister Judy, her husband Dan and very close friend Jacquie Rogers.

AC/DC kicked off the New Year in Tasmania on 7 January, the day after Mal's twenty-fourth birthday. We played Hobart, Launceston and Burnie without any trouble, before returning to the mainland to continue the tour in the Victorian country town of Horsham. Then it was back to shit-shower time. The mayor of Warrnambool decided we were—drum roll, please—'disgusting', and barred us from disturbing his town's peace. This was getting way beyond a joke and it was about this point where we all may have come to the same conclusion—'Fuck it, we do not need this,'—and duly crossed the entire country off our Christmas card list.

It was just getting too stupid for words, although Angus had a few choice ones for the newspapers. 'It's no good,' he said, 'if we drive halfway across the country to stage a concert to find someone has cancelled it because they consider us obscene. It will only take a couple more hassles from the authorities and we will leave Australia.'

Still, like the troopers we were, we trundled through regional Victoria without much more bother, to finally play the Festival Hall in Melbourne on 15 January. The attendance was somewhat disappointing; it was a respectable turnout but nowhere near the sellout that we would have liked (and that the promoters Gudinski/Evans would have preferred too, no doubt). The theory was that the negative press was beginning to bite. Maybe, but I thought the band could well have outgrown its former teenybopper crowd, who may have jumped ship. A lot can happen to a band in a couple of weeks.

The gig ripped anyway, the band was on fire, but I noticed that since we got back on the road from our Christmas break there was a perceptible change in atmosphere. I put it down to the grief we were getting in the press and the problems that were cropping up in the States, where the *Dirty Deeds* album had been knocked back by the ATCO label. Still, there was a distinct chill in the air.

So it was with some relief we decided to 'kick on' after the gig, back at our hotel, Noah's on Exhibition Street in the city. It was a big night of booze and other party favours supplied by acquaintances back at the hotel. But it was also memorable for an entirely different reason—it was only the third time I saw Angus drink alcohol. Needless to say, the effect was quick and quite dramatic. Angus was briefly the life of the party, complete with singing and dancing, then he mellowed out and got all philosophical and reflective.

At one point he collared me and was surprisingly interested in how I was feeling, being back in my hometown. He extracted an undertaking from me that I would spend as much time as I could with my family while in Melbourne. I was pleased to be speaking with him on such a personal level. I clearly recall making one comment: 'You should hit the bottle more often, Angus.' I was enjoying his newfound warmth, and the comment seemed to please him. We rattled on for a while until the party ran out of steam and we decided to move on.

It was as I was leaving that Angus pulled me aside.

'Mal isn't happy with the way you're doing things,' he said. 'It's not a problem for me, but you should take it up with Mal.'

Angus was clearly under the influence, but he seemed sincere. I left the hotel that night decidedly uneasy. To say Angus had me scratching my head was an understatement.

The next morning I called Mal to set up a meeting over lunch in a restaurant across the other side of Exhibition Street.

'Mal, do you have a problem?' I asked him, point blank.

'That's not what I think,' he replied. 'That's Angus saying that.'

I began to think that Angus had been bullshitting me and that Mal was being straight, as I'd come to expect from him. It became apparent to me soon enough, though, that Malcolm was bullshitting me too. I would have preferred to know the truth, but that either didn't suit the Youngs, or Malcolm just didn't have the bottle to play it straight. I still feel disappointed when I think of that meeting; it was a real turning point for me, although I didn't realise it at the time. I was on the way out of the band but just wasn't smart enough to pick it up. I swallowed what Malcolm told me along with the very average spaghetti bolognese. I walked out of the restaurant with Mal thinking that Angus had played me for a goose. Well, as I would find out in the very near future, they both got me good.

ϟ

We had one more show to do in Victoria before we flew back to Sydney. It was in Moe, west of Melbourne, in the Gippsland region. My strongest memory of the gig was the crowd, or should I say the crowd reaction. There was none. When I say none, I mean nothing, zero. Not even a cough after a song; just absolute silence. It was weird and I have no idea what caused it. It was one of the strangest gigs I have ever played, not just with AC/DC but in my entire career. We'd be blazing away, a tune would come to a resounding, crashing finish—and then nothing.

We soldiered on, and even though our crew was growing increasingly disgruntled, Bon and Angus still went at it as if we were playing to 10,000 feral AC/DC fans. We got to the end of 'Baby Please Don't Go', featuring all of Angus's usual antics, and left the stage to almost total silence. The crew then marched out on stage en masse, lined up, dropped their jeans and gave the folks of Moe a good look at a dozen bare roadie arses.

What a way to wind up that leg of the Giant Dose tour. One wag on the crew dubbed it the 'Giant Pain in the Arse' tour and it was hard to argue with him. We were relieved to be heading to Sydney and into Alberts to start on the new album with George and Harry. This was to be the third and final album I'd record with AC/DC, along with some other one-off sessions to record 'Jailbreak' and 'Fling Thing', and a session at the Vineyard Studios in London to put down 'Love at First Feel' and 'Carry Me Home'—songs that still didn't make the Americans love us, as we were now discovering. All this studio time would occur within about eighteen months. It was an unbelievable workload, virtually unheard of these days.

Dirty Deeds had been released in Australia late 1976 to coincide with our Giant Dose tour. Even though we were about to begin work on a new album, its predecessor, recorded close to a year ago, was not yet released in some major markets and had only been out in Australia for a couple of months.

The *Dirty Deeds* LP created a lot less excitement with ATCO, our US record company, than we hoped for. They were lukewarm at best and this started causing problems for us Stateside. News filtered back that they weren't pleased with the production of the record and that the songs weren't strong enough, even after we went into the studio in London to put down extra tracks. It all came to a head and eventually they 'passed' on it, refusing to release it. Thank you very fuckin' much. Over the Christmas/New Year period, Michael

Browning and the head of Atlantic Records in London, Phil Carson, had to fight a rearguard action purely to keep our US deal afloat. Things were looking very shaky for the band in America. It was implicit that we had better come up with the goods in the studio this time round, or suffer the not-too-appealing consequences.

Both the issues with ATCO and the crap surrounding the Giant Dose tour were taking their toll. I'm not saying self-doubt was creeping in, that wasn't part of the AC/DC manifesto, but questions were being asked. What were the Yanks up to, knocking back *Dirty Deeds*? I'm sure that George and Harry were less than pleased at having their production criticised. When we returned to the studio, the prevailing attitude was simple. 'Fuck 'em. Let's see them knock this one back.'

We commenced recording in mid-January, and stuck with the usual routine. Mal, Angus and George worked on the riffs, bits and pieces that had been stockpiled while we were on the road. The tunes developed to the point where the band would start blowing on the idea, getting the arrangement sitting comfortably, and if it was working, roll the tape and get it down. If that sounds simple, well, it was. If the tune was swinging, it would grow legs and come to life. If an idea got bogged down, it was a good indication it just wasn't going to work, or might be worth revisiting down the line. What I learned from George and Harry is that you had to have a track that grooves; that's the essence of a great record. If you don't have that, forget it, you have zero, move on to something else, you're wasting your time.

As with all the AC/DC recordings with which I was involved, we were working to a tight schedule. Two weeks to write, arrange and record an album. That's some sort of effort. While I wasn't involved in the writing and arranging, what I'm saying is that it was a mammoth effort by Mal, Angus and Bon to put the material together in such a short time, with George and Harry also getting their hands pretty dirty. Astounding stuff, especially when you consider the quality of the songs, some of them stone-cold classics that still feature in the AC/DC live set.

We had a week and a bit to get the backing tracks down, the same time for the vocals, solos and any patching up that was necessary. The studio drill was really an extension of the band live: cut the crap and get on with it. As the tracks were coming together, early versions were put onto a cassette (remember those things?) and given to Bon. He would delve into his notebooks of 'dirty ditties' and possible song titles while, supposedly, locked away in the kitchen at Alberts.

I was bloody lucky. I was getting an amazing inside view on how to put a rock and roll record together, and in a fuckin' hurry, too. Recording what was to become *Let There Be Rock* necessitated the same 'hothouse' conditions as *TNT* and *Dirty Deeds*: get in there and get it done, today. Unlike my first session with the band, where I was an enthusiastic onlooker, I was now in the studio with the guys, putting down my parts. George was playing much less of a mentoring role, but if he had an angle for a song, no worries, George, here's my bass. I would have been an absolute idiot to do otherwise. When George spoke, I listened.

One of the first tracks to get a workout was 'Bad Boy Boogie'. BBB was a rarity, a tune that we had messed around with beforehand. The band had worked up the groove during a few sound checks, including the Festival Hall show on

15 January. As we were walking off the stage, one of the crew asked me what the song was called. I answered 'Black Sheep Boogie'—I was and still am positive I had heard the song referred to that way. Angus was quick to correct me.

'It's "Bad Boy Boogie", and I oughta know.'

'Okay then, make that "Bad Boy Boogie",' I said. 'He knows everything.'

This was supposed to land a lot lighter than it obviously did with Angus. He shot me a look that made me want to rush back to the hotel and take a shower. Sometimes it would have been a lot smarter of me just to shut the fuck up and not try to be the comedian. That still stands for me these days, actually.

Another track to come together quickly was 'Go Down'. That had a great groove from the get-go and was tagged as a possible opening track very early on. It's probably one of the lesser-known tracks from that period but it's a cracker, the guitars are magic. A personal favourite of mine was 'Hell Ain't a Bad Place to Be'. That was another from early on in the sessions. The guitars rip, it's a real teeth-rattler, but not if you're a stickler for things being perfectly in tune. But when you get a groove like that, fuck it, who cares about tuning?

The high point of the recording was the title track, 'Let There Be Rock'. That's an epic, with Phil going flat to the boards for the entire six-plus minutes. Watching him cut that one in the studio was amazing. He was set up in the back left-hand corner of the piano room, opposite the wall with all the graffiti, and he just went for it. We did a couple of takes in a row, with just a quick breather between the two, a minute at the most, and away we went again. It's my recollection that we used the second of those two takes. Phil's importance to the band's sound cannot be overestimated in my books. Take him out of the line-up and it just doesn't sound right to me. But I'm biased, obviously.

The pressure was really on to deliver a great AC/DC album. And *Let There Be Rock* was the sound of us stepping up. A hell of a lot had happened to AC/DC since recording *Dirty Deeds Done Dirt Cheap*. All that touring had changed us. Our new back line of Marshall gear gave the band more muscle; we sounded more aggressive, meaner—and definitely louder. The band started to sound like the AC/DC that the world has come to know. There was more of an edge to the sound; it was a bigger, badder AC/DC.

It's still one of my favourite AC/DC albums, just behind *Powerage* and my all-time favourite, *Highway to Hell*. I make no excuses for preferring the albums with Bon out front, with all due respect to Brian Johnson. The character of Bon's voice and his lyrics—what can you say? He was born to be the singer in AC/DC.

On 30 January we took a break from recording in Alberts and travelled all of a mile west to George Street, Sydney's main drag, to headline a show for the Festival of Sydney at the Haymarket. This was one of the major gigs on the 'Giant Pain in the Arse' tour that was both filmed and recorded. We had a full film crew travel with us on selected gigs, headed by Russell Mulcahy, who directed the film *Razorback* (and later on shot videos for Duran Duran, but I won't hold that against him). He and his crew shot hours of on-the-road stuff along with gig footage. (Further down the line, we all sat down at a studio in North Sydney to view a 'rough cut' of a doco put together by Russell. That doco is still sitting around somewhere in the vaults, I guess.)

Let There Be Rock was left in the safe hands of George and Harry to mix. We had a few gigs to tidy up before we could make what was starting to feel like an escape from Australia. There was a vibe starting to build among us that it was time to get back to unfinished business in the UK, Europe and eventually the US. The sooner the better as far as I was concerned. I was dying to get to America.

We played Adelaide on 12 February and the Perth Entertainment Centre on Sunday 13 February, which gave Bon the chance to pay a long-overdue visit to his folks. He introduced them to Silver, who'd joined him on the tour. His people would have been overjoyed to see Ron—as he was known in the family circle—but I have no idea what Chick and Isa, his parents, would have made of Silver. I figure that if Ron was happy that suited them well enough, within the boundaries of a staid Scots family's sense of decorum, of course. Isa had made it clear, however, that she would like her eldest son to write some 'nicer' lyrics.

The Perth show was our 'see you later, Australia' gig. It was a good one, too; we got a great reaction and the band was kicking, perhaps fuelled by the relief that our troubled sojourn was now all but over. The gig was a memorable one for me. We used the freshly recorded 'Dog Eat Dog' as an encore, and I indulged in a bit of gear trashing, giving the hired bass rig the ol' heave-ho. It went crashing over backwards, much to the delight of Angus but to the dismay of the promoter's tour manager, Ian Smith.

As I exited the stage, Ian got me in a headlock. 'You'll pay for that, you little prick!' he screamed. Ian was typically a very polite, docile gentleman, who, until I trashed the rented gear, must have been as relieved as us that we'd made it to the end of a tough tour. You didn't think I'd trash our own stuff, did you?

It was Bon's last gig in Perth.

We flew out late on the afternoon of Monday, 14 February, which gave those brave enough plenty of time to enjoy some sailing on Perth's beautiful Swan River. It was a typically hot, clear Perth day on the river, or so I was told. I was nursing a motherfucker of a hangover and didn't get to see much of it. It was one of those deadly hangovers where if you move your head, your brain lags heavily behind, shifting around like an egg yolk inside its shell. The jungle drums thumping inside my skull would only back off when I was completely submerged in the hotel pool.

So I spent as much of the day as humanly possible on the bottom of the pool, much to the consternation of the hotel staff. The yachties had a ball, apparently; they got back to the hotel with only just enough time to grab their bags and hit the airport, still in their sailing gear, smelling of salt water and sunburn. I can't begin to tell you how out of place a group of sun-blasted blokes in shorts, T-shirts and thongs looked at Heathrow Airport on a crisp mid-February morning.

Chapter 10

'Eddie and the Hot Rods are looking for a bass player'

We hit the ground running, or so it seemed anyway. We relocated again, moving into a couple of flats in Ladbroke Grove. Mal and Angus shared one and Phil and I were close by, near Portobello Road and its famous markets. We had a day to get settled then it was north to Edinburgh to open the Dirty Deeds Done Dirt Cheap tour on 18 February. Like I said, AC/DC was a juggernaut that never stopped rolling.

The tour was a twenty-six-date run in support of the new UK release, which, like *High Voltage*, wasn't setting the charts on fire. It was becoming apparent that while we were making good ground at street level, with the punters, the all-important radio airplay and TV exposure was very slow in coming. So we had to stick with the tried-and-true AC/DC way: gigs, gigs and even more gigs.

Our seemingly endless work schedule shaped our way of thinking, united us (or that's what I thought) and helped foster the 'AC/DC vs the Rest of the World' outlook that we thrived on. We always seemed to be going into new territories as a virtually unknown band and there was no better way to stay grounded than that. There was no chance of getting carried away by the little success we had because it was guaranteed we'd soon be somewhere where we meant absolutely fuck-all and had to set about converting people all over again. And if there was ever any 'pop starring', the offending party would get jumped on very quickly. The standard line was: 'Who the fuck do you think you are, xxxxxx?' You could fill in the space with Frank Sinatra, Jimi Hendrix, Ringo Starr, Paul McCartney or whoever best fitted the situation.

The Dirty Deeds tour took us to a variety of venues: unis, polytechs, ballrooms and clubs (we played a load of clubs called 'Top Rank Suite'). The venues would reflect how strong—or otherwise—we were in the particular area. We opened at Edinburgh and Glasgow, both strongly attended uni gigs, but as we headed south we ventured into less fertile AC/DC territory. The response ranged from rapturous to 'who gives a fuck' and the quality of the venues from excellent to absolute shithouses.

The lower end of the scale—and believe me, there was no lower—was the Electric Circus in Manchester. This place should have been condemned, probably was in the end. It was a small, dingy, dark hole-in-the-wall type of joint, an unmitigated dump. The stage was cramped and very damp, not all that reassuring when you're working with the amount of electricity that was needed to power up AC/DC.

The so-called band room was a cracker—it was an enclosed platform that was jerrybuilt over the bar and had been enclosed on three sides, so it looked down on the electrical death trap of a stage. Naturally, it was small and smelly (perfect for AC/DC, you might say). This poor excuse for a band room was accessed by climbing a rickety old ladder by the bar. The clincher was the toilets, so skunky they made you want to go anywhere else in the known universe just to take a piss. The aroma was a peculiar combination of crap with marine overtones, possibly seaweed—odd, really, since Manchester is inland. I remember zilch about the show but the Electric Circus is indelibly etched into both my memory and olfactory nerve.

There were few landmark gigs on the Dirty Deeds tour, although one did have a historic ring to it. The Who recorded their magnificent *Live at Leeds* LP at Leeds University in 1970. *Live at Leeds* was mandatory listening for my generation (see what I did there?) of prospective rockers and, I hazard to say, a generation or so after as well. For AC/DC to be playing the same gig, well, that was something else for me as a card-carrying Who fan. *Live at Leeds* was a real big deal and the perception for me, from 16,000 kilometres away, was that Leeds University must have also been a big deal. Come on, The Who played there! Well, here was AC/DC playing the same gig and the hall held around 1000 punters at a squeeze. Was this even the same venue? It brought home the fact that we weren't all that far separated from the big boys, mainly because the big boys might not have been quite as big or as far out in front as we once thought.

Angus was the most dedicated musician I've ever encountered in my career, so it was a real surprise that the award for 'closest the band ever went to blowing a gig out due to someone's overindulgence' goes to—who'd have thought?—Angus Young. It was 10 March, nearing the end of the Dirty Deeds tour, and we were to play at St Andrews Hall in Norwich, three hours north-east of London. This was one of two venues that were booked by a couple of East End characters from Walthamstow. I can't recall their names, probably because of the very healthy hospitality they used to supply. It was always a feature at Norwich and their other gig, the Cambridge Corn Exchange.

We were scheduled to leave our London digs just after lunch to give us enough time for the drive, sound check and the usual pre-gig routine. But departure was delayed, delayed further, then delayed again because of an Angus Young hangover, an occurrence almost as rare as Halley's Comet. It was a beauty, too. For the life of me I can't recall what possessed Angus to hit the sauce but the few times I'd seen him drunk it was just a spur of the moment thing and—BANG! He would launch into it. I have a sneaking suspicion there might have been a cute young lady involved. Now, his tolerance was very low, but lower still was his tolerance to hangovers. In my time with AC/DC he was never an early riser, but when loaded up with a monster hangover, Angus wasn't going anywhere.

'Fuck the gig,' he moaned, and pulled the covers over his head.

There was much cajoling from Malcolm, while Phil and I waited nearby. Mal would give us progress reports—nope, it wasn't looking good for Norwich. Mal was getting frustrated with his younger brother, so much so that he even suggested that I should have a go at convincing Angus to get his shit together. Phil burst into laughter. It was a ridiculous idea, after all.

But I've always relished a challenge, so down the stairs I went, while Mal hung back with Phil. I knocked on Angus's door and stuck my head into his darkened room. It stank of vomit. Before I could offer him a cuppa, I heard a disembodied whimper. 'Fuck off.'

Well, I figured, let's give it a go anyway. 'Hey, Angus, how about a . . .'

'FUCK OFF!'

That was it for me. I reported back to Mal and Phil that the gig wasn't looking all that flash. Finally, Mal got Angus mobile and into the car for some Rudd 'low flying' to Norwich. Angus was positively green around the gills, and didn't say a word all the way there. He stayed that way until we walked on stage. But I started up the bass intro to 'Livewire', away we went and Angus cranked it up. He was as sick as a dog but he let it rip as usual. The manic schoolboy might have missed our start time, but he'd never blow out a gig.

Dirty Deeds rolled on to London, where our showcase gig wasn't the Hammersmith Odeon, but the Rainbow in Finsbury Park, on 11 March. The gig was reasonably well attended, though not a sellout. For some reason, the crowd, while very receptive, didn't go over the top as we'd expected. We'd had a few technical hassles that can make any band a bit snaky. This, combined with the crowd's less than crazy response, left us with a flat feeling about the show. This was more than obvious in the band room après gig; it was deadly quiet.

This is where I believe I made another bad call. It would have been wise for me to stick around for the post-mortem, no matter what went down. But I didn't. I had a couple of pals waiting in the backstage bar and I certainly wasn't bringing them into the band room, which had all the vibe of a morgue. Another reason I hit the door hard, fast and a little prematurely was that things had been a little strained in the last week or so leading up to that Rainbow show.

My twenty-first birthday fell on 2 March 1977. We were booked to play in Swansea, Wales, but for one reason or another the gig got blown out. With Coral Browning heading the social committee, the guys threw a surprise party for me in London. They rounded me up early in the evening, and Phil, Mal and I tipped ourselves into a cab. I'd already had a few with Mal. Okay, maybe I'd had more than a few. We ended up in a German bierkeller, somewhere in Maida Vale, I think. Our pals, the Barnes dustmen, were there, along with record company people, our crew, my American girlfriend Risa and a few other people who had managed to infiltrate AC/DC's force field, searchlights and machine-gun turrets.

The night was progressing pretty well. I loathed birthday celebrations and had managed, so far, to avoid them during my tenure with the band. I despised the experience of having people sing 'Happy Birthday' to me, and do to this very day. I let people know that if they felt the need to sing anything to me, then belt out the Carlton Football Club song. The best explanation for this I can come up with is an experience I had when I was three years old, and we'd been celebrating my sister Judy's eighth birthday. Early the next morning I spotted the remainder of her cake, complete with candles, on top of the fridge. I decided it was a good idea to throw myself a birthday party, so I pulled up a stool and started to light the candles, starting at the front. But as I reached over to light the candles at the back, my pyjamas caught fire. My mother heard my screams, ran downstairs to the kitchen and put me out. That's my first vivid memory: being on fire. Thanks to lots of cold water and the first aid of the local chemist I am not visibly scarred. So sing 'Happy Birthday' to me and I cringe. Singe, maybe.

So here I was on my twenty-first in London, dreading the song. I was at the bar with Paul 'Scotty' Wright, our tour manager and pal, and his brother. We were chatting away, hitting the turps. Scotty's brother was quizzing me about the band, asking some odd questions that I put down to the beer. Then he came out with it.

'You all seem to get on great. How come you're leaving the band?'

Huh? I turned to Scotty, who looked like someone had shot him. We stood there in silence for a bit and then Scotty asked me to join him outside. There we were on the sidewalk outside the bierkeller, which I still think is in Maida Vale.

'What the fuck is going on, Scotty?' I asked.

By this stage, Scotty was pissed, in tears and past the point of caring about protocol.

'You can't trust them, Mark.'

That was all he managed to get out.

What I should have done was go back inside and sort it out, or at least sort it out the next day. Either way, I should have gone back in—it was my twenty-first birthday party, for fuck's sake. Instead I hailed a taxi and took Scotty and his brother to dinner and a few more drinks at the Speakeasy, leaving the party to take care of itself. At least I managed to dodge being serenaded with 'Happy Birthday'. Happy fuckin' birthday, indeed.

By early April 1977 we were in Paris, starting a European tour supporting Black Sabbath, fronted by Ozzy Osbourne, the Prince Of Darkness or, as he was wont to call himself, the

Plumber of Darkness, a nod to his pre-Sabbath vocation. The tour swept through France, Germany, Switzerland, Denmark, Belgium, Holland, Sweden and Norway before finishing in Helsinki, Finland on 24 April. Then we were to fly directly to the US. We were busy boys again, just how we liked it.

There'd been no mention of my early exit from my twenty-first in London. I was relieved because I felt pretty shabby about it. It was bad form under any circumstances. I just hoped some wires had got crossed and that Scotty had somehow made a mistake. Anyway, the dust had settled and it was now back to work. Or at least that's what I was thinking and I'd neither heard nor seen anything to make me think otherwise. Those words of Scotty's were still nagging, though. I'd dream that I got sacked from the band and I'd wake up feeling sick to my stomach.

Black Sabbath had been one of my favourite bands in the early seventies, along with Deep Purple. They drifted off my radar when I discovered Free and rediscovered the Stones but I was still dead keen to see what Sabbath had to offer. Their style of 'doomsday' heavy rock was dating rapidly under the pressure of punk rock and the coming of the New Wave bands, but that didn't stop me looking on with some interest from side stage at the first gig in Paris.

It didn't take me long to note that they were off their game. It may have been the first night of the tour but at times it was shambolic. It was loud, noisy and messy; it just wasn't punching. These guys deserved a load of respect for what they had achieved but to me it looked like time was running out for Sabbath. I'm sure no one was impressed. On the Rainbow tour you had Blackmore playing as only he could, Cozy Powell laying it down and the coughing, spluttering electric rainbow to add a few laughs. But for me, Sabbath's only redeeming feature was Ozzy, who, in his own very unique way, lurched almost robotically from side to side of the stage. He was certainly no great mover or shaker but he was Ozzy, a real character and the guy leading the charge.

I think we definitely got offside with Sabbath's bass player Geezer Butler. Some of us would gather side of stage to cheer him on during his bass solo (why the fuck anyone needed a bass solo is beyond me, but anyway). It all started out good-natured enough, but as the tour wore on and we richly cheered a couple of his clangers, it got a bit testy. In defence of the cheer squad, there was no malice intended and, frankly, if you set yourself up to play a bass solo in front of a few thousand paying punters, best get it right. But he was one unhappy Geezer.

Quickly we slipped back into the normal AC/DC touring routine: be in the hotel lobby on time to get on the bus, take a nap or bury your head in a book, or a comic in Bon's case. The band was firing and going over very well. Nothing we'd seen or heard from Sabbath fazed us. If anything, it was the opposite—what they were offering made us more confident in our potential, and even more arrogant. Our sole aim became this: get on stage every night and blow Sabbath sky fuckin' high. That might sound egotistical but a support band's mission is to try and get ahead, every night.

Word had started filtering down the line (the line where I stood way down the end, holding the door open for the others) that the US departure from Helsinki was looking flaky. Teeth were gnashed. There was still a fair bit of angst regarding *Dirty Deeds Done Dirt Cheap* getting the flick by ATCO in the US; we were eager to set the Yanks straight.

Things then started getting ugly. We had a night out in Copenhagen with the local Atlantic Records rep, who was a very polite guy but a tad sheepish. We started off at the hotel bar and by the time we left for the red-light district we were seriously warmed up. We checked out some of the ladies and hit another bar for refreshments. As we came out of the bar we crossed paths with some equally drunk Germans and, well, one thing led to another. One of the Germans took a definite dislike to me and wanted to punch my lights out. I wasn't all that keen, but that didn't stop Phil.

'Knock his fuckin' head off, Herbie!' Phil suggested.

The German was shaping up, but I was telling him, and gesturing, that he should go home. My message must have got lost in translation. I knew the signs well enough to know he was about to bring it, so I whacked him smack on the jaw with a strong left. As he was going backwards I gave him a massive kick in the nuts. He was gone, down and puking. Michael Browning belted another one but broke a finger in the process. Our record company guy, meanwhile, was probably thinking about early retirement. But Phil was revved up.

'Let's get some more!'

No thanks, Phil, just put one out.

And it was fisticuffs, or near fisticuffs, that spelled the end of the Black Sabbath tour for AC/DC. I can't give a reliable first-hand report because I wasn't there—and probably just as well. We were in Brussels (I think; I was hitting the Scotch pretty hard again) and in a very unusual and uncharacteristic course of events Mal ended up at the hotel where Sabbath was staying. This was right out of character and I have absolutely no idea how it came about, but I would guess he was well tanked up. I was told that Geezer Butler took exception to something Mal said and pulled a knife on him. The story goes that Mal belted him and that was it. What I do know was the next morning Mal was so contrite that he returned to their hotel and apologised for the night before, which was again right out of character.

One thing was for sure: our Black Sabbath tour was over, as were our immediate plans to go to the US. We had hit a couple of serious bumps in the road and the *esprit de corps* was not all that spry. So rather than continuing on to America we slinked back to London. The natives were getting restless but I couldn't hear the jungle drums.

ϟ

We were back in London with time on our hands. It was spring but to this Aussie it was still mind-numbingly cold. And it sure didn't feel like a year had passed since we'd first landed in the UK. Yet in that time we'd recorded an album, toured Australia yet again, Europe twice, been to Sweden and journeyed up and down the length and breadth of the UK ad infinitum.

Our American plans were still on hold, so it was time to cool our heels. I was getting very familiar with London, especially the city and the West End. I never tired of jumping on the tube from Notting Hill Gate for the short trip into Piccadilly Circus or Trafalgar Square. I'd emerge into the sunlight and be surrounded by London: Nelson's Column, red double-decker buses, bobbies, the works. I'd look back over my shoulder through Admiralty Arch, walk down The Mall to Buckingham Palace or glance down Whitehall to Big Ben. These were the landmarks I used to dream about when I was a child. London was starting to feel like home—but for how long? This week? Today, anyway.

I spent some of my time and a stack more of my dough in the guitar stores on Denmark Street and Shaftesbury Avenue. I was developing a passion for classic basses and guitars. Little did I know it was the start of an intriguing and continuing journey.

Helping to fill in some of my spare time was Ellen, a young lady I'd met in Stockholm. She had decided to make a flying visit to London and had tracked me down via the Marquee people. I'd first met her the year before, when she was barely eighteen. I spotted her outside our Stockholm digs, the Hotel Alexandra, and was struck by how stunning she was. Ellen was much taller than me (not hard, that), very reserved and cool, but not classically Nordic because of her long, dark curly hair.

Our relationship appeared doomed within minutes. She knew little English and my Swedish comprised of such on-the-road standards as: 'Four beers, please', 'Which way to the toilet?' and that old standby, 'That's a nice pair of boobs you have there, sweetheart.' The first two were of no use in Ellen's case but the last definitely applied. When I first saw her, her boobs were almost directly in my eyeline—well, I had to look down a bit and got caught, of course. She gave me a cheeky smile and the language hitch wasn't much of an issue after that.

It was a tad tricky later that night at her family home. Not much English was spoken there either, but there were plenty of Swedish meatballs and some great beer with Dad. It was getting late, rolling on to 10.30 pm, but it was still light outside. And I had no idea where I was. Should I try and arrange a cab? And if so, just how the fuck would I do that? Silly me—I should have factored in some very liberal Scandinavian thinking. It soon became clear that I was to stay over with Ellen—and I mean *with* Ellen. Later that night it was with due respect to her folks that we tried to keep the noise down during a few lively rounds of horizontal Swedish folk dancing.

When Ellen found me in London a year later, her English had improved marginally, my Swedish still sucked and she was even more of a knockout. After an especially big one at the Speak, where I spent most of the night doing my level best to peel half the guitarists/drummers/singers/bass players in the joint off her, much to her amusement, I retired to Ellen's hotel in Soho.

'Mack, you have so many friends!' she said with a smile.

Did I mention she couldn't say Mark? I was Mack. Fine by me. Better than Mike.

There was a sign in her hotel lobby that read: NO GUESTS TO BE TAKEN TO HOTEL SUITES. No one takes those signs seriously, do they? I had just endured hours of hand-to-hand combat at the Speakeasy keeping those dirty fuckers off Ellen. I was staying.

However, we were rudely awoken in the morning by a female blimp with a ripping Cockney accent bellowing: 'No guests in 'ere!' It could have been Eliza Doolittle's fat-arsed granddaughter, I swear. Two house detectives promptly arrived and they ordered me to get dressed.

'You're nicked, son!'

I had no option but to burst into fits of laughter. Fuck me, it's the Sweeney! I kissed Ellen goodbye and made her promise to visit me in the Tower of London. She didn't get it but Dumb and Dumber did—and they didn't like it.

'You're in a lot of trouble, my boy,' they announced, frog-marching me through the lobby like I was Ronnie Biggs.

What the fuck! This was ridiculous. I couldn't help it; this was getting funnier by the minute. So I started to struggle a bit and yelled: 'DON'T HIT ME AGAIN! I'LL PAY YOU! JUST DON'T HIT ME AGAIN!' Dumber started looking around at the other hotel guests, who were getting a little nervous. 'We didn't 'it 'im, honest,' he said, raising his hands in innocence.

They pushed me into the office, where the shakedown began.

'We could fit you up with anything and get the coppers in,' said B1.

'It's twenty-five quid a night here, you know,' B2 threw in.

I thought this over. 'How about I give you twenty-five quid each and we'll call it quits?'

They chewed this over. 'No, just the twenty-five is fine. We'll split it.'

Fuckin' hell! I almost felt like insisting on twenty-five quid each for the entertainment. How did these morons get employed? I peeled off the pounds from a roll of old guitar money I was going to spend that day and they nearly passed out.

'Gee, you South Africans carry a lot of cash about.'

I was back upstairs and straight into the sack with Ellen in a flash.

ϟ

When Ellen finally left to go back to Stockholm, I was in the mood for a night out, so I asked Phil if he wanted to join me. He said no. This puzzled me; he had just got out of the shower and appeared to be getting ready to go somewhere.

'You sure?' I asked again, keen to tag along.

'No, mate, I'm staying in.'

I figured he had a girl coming over so I hit the tube into Soho and the Marquee. The band playing at the Marquee sucked, so I had a couple of beers with Simon, the bar manager, and drifted off to another watering hole on Wardour Street, the Ship. More beer, Scotch and darts with the locals ensued. Then I was off to the Speak. The band there sucked, too, but I found time for a few with the Speakeasy barflies (I guessed that now included me) before heading into the restaurant for a decent steak and a nightcap, first checking that Sex Pistol Steve wasn't in there to ambush my dinner. This was where things started to get weird.

I left the restaurant and ordered a beer and a Scotch and spotted Michael Browning, Mal and Angus on the other side of the bar. What the fuck was this? Angus out—*at a bar?* Something was up. I waved but got no reaction. I called out, again nothing. Michael had left the bar by this time, probably to take a piss—I'm not sure he saw me—but Mal and Angus certainly did. Okay then guys, be that way. Fuck it. I ordered up again.

The next morning, Phil told me there was a meeting at Mal and Angus's place up the road. Unusual again, but sure, whatever.

'Hey, Phil,' I asked him. 'What did you get up to last night? You look like crap.'

'Nothing mate, nothing.'

'I saw Mal and Angus out with Browning at the Speakeasy last night. Weird, eh?' I continued.

Phil stood there in his jocks, not saying a thing. His face was as white as a ghost.

Phil and I walked to Mal and Angus's flat. It was a really nice day, dead quiet. We didn't say a word to each other during the walk. We didn't have to. I had a pretty fair idea what was coming. We knocked and entered. Michael and Bon were there, too. Shit. Michael was sitting at the dining table next to the kitchen door. Mal, Angus and Bon were on the couch. Phil sat down on a chair next to Bon, leaving a chair at the table, nearest the kitchen door, for me.

'Let me get you a cuppa,' said Michael, who headed off to the kitchen.

This was getting weirder. Phil was leaning forward, hands clasped, elbows on his knees, staring at the floor. Bon was leaning back on the couch with his arms folded, looking at the ceiling. He looked at me once and shook his head. Mal and Angus sat there quietly, squashed up tightly together, almost joined at the hip.

Michael returned with my tea and started the conversation.

'Mark, this meeting is mainly about you.'

Mainly?

'Malcolm . . . the guys, the band, want to get another bass player.'

Fuck, I was going to throw up.

'What do you think, Mark?'

Why was he asking me what I thought? I was getting the bullet from the band, my mates. What the fuck did he think was going through my mind?

When I spoke, it was as though the words were coming out of someone else's mouth.

'If that's what the guys want, Michael.'

But fuck, this was the last thing *I* wanted.

Bon was the next to speak up. He leaned forward. 'Mark, you have to understand that it is nothing personal, it's a . . .' He trailed off. He was looking straight at me, but then he looked away and shook his head again.

Then it was Mal's turn. 'We want to get a bass player who can sing. That's all.'

Phil, finally, looked up at me and simply shrugged his shoulders. He was telling me what I knew already. There was nothing he could do. Angus didn't say or do a thing. Not one look, word, glance. Nothing. Zilch. Zero.

I went to pick up my cup of tea but I was shaking like a leaf. I literally couldn't get the cup to my mouth. It wasn't a surprise but it was a hell of a shock. I was blown to bits, absolutely shattered. Until then I'd been living the dream. Now I was in the middle of a nightmare.

I couldn't get out of there fast enough. Michael suggested I go back to his place in Ebury Mews to 'make arrangements'. And what exactly did that mean? Michael and I got a cab on the street and talked on the way to his home-cum-office. I was still in a daze. I'd been boned by my own band. He told me that he thought the meeting the night before at the Speak was going to be about Bon and the pressure that was coming from the US about our, sorry, *their* singer.

'I'm really surprised it was about you, Mark. I'm truly sorry.'

But it was none of his doing, I knew that. What Michael should have apologised for was what he said next.

'I hear that Eddie and the Hot Rods are looking for a bass player. What do you reckon, Mark?'

My look said it all, I'm sure. I could feel that cup of tea on its way up again. I felt exactly the same as I did when I woke from my dreams of being sacked by the guys—absolutely sick to my stomach.

Could I salvage the situation? I asked myself. Maybe I could ask the guys for a little more rope, and if I hanged myself, so be it. And why the fuck hadn't I spoken up at the meeting? My future had gone down the shitter and I'd just sat there and let it happen.

I asked Michael whether he thought they'd give me another chance.

He gave it some thought. 'Mark, do you really want to continue on like this?'

I was looking out the cab window at London's West End sliding by, pondering Michael's very astute reply, when suddenly I felt all the recent ill-feeling, angst and turmoil flush out of my body in a massive rush. I could almost hear it, taste it. I felt this huge weight drop off my shoulders. In a heartbeat I had this wonderful feeling of relief and wellbeing. This cab was heading in the right direction, away from the guys. Sure I was devastated, but there was no point going back to the band with some kind of pathetic appeal. I was out on my arse and the sooner I dusted myself off the better.

I turned to Michael. 'Get me on the first flight to Melbourne, will ya?'

ϟ

It was a very poignant moment for me, saying 'see you later' to Mal and Phil at Heathrow. To their eternal credit, they'd offered to drive me to the airport and have a quiet one before tipping me onto the flight to Melbourne. Nice gesture and I appreciated it.

Undertakings were made to catch up back in Australia or wherever else it might be. Mal thanked me, wished me well and said he hoped there were no hard feelings. Phil had regained some colour in his face since the meeting but now he was looking a tad shaky again. Me too. It was a sad moment; I sensed that Phil was doing it as tough as I was. I realised that I was going to miss these two immensely; we'd been through so much together, but it was rankling that I was now deemed redundant. I'd been kicked out of the gang. I'd had a day or so to digest what had happened and I was gutted, but at the same time relieved to be out of the pressure cooker. I was coming to terms with the fact that if I had been the right guy for the gig, well, I would still be in the band.

I'd said my goodbyes to Bon the night before. Bon and Silver had offered their place as a base if I wanted to stay on in London.

'You'll be going backwards if you go home,' Bon said. 'Look for another gig here. You never know what could happen, Mark.' Those were his exact words. They'd prove to be sadly prescient in Bon's case.

It was my plan to return to London after some rest and recreation in Melbourne. My mum's birthday was on 2 May and I wanted to surprise her by showing up. I told Bon that I'd take up his offer when I returned. Bon said that Silver could use the company when he was away but I was sure that was about as far from the truth as possible. I think Bon was telling me he wanted our friendship to continue. He was being typically Bon, wanting to lend a hand to someone he saw was hurting badly.

I settled in on the plane. I had plenty of time to reflect on what had happened and the last thing on my mind was my future. I was still jarred by just how rapid my exit had been. One moment I was gearing up for a long-awaited visit to the US and then the axe fell. I felt dead inside. I truly did. Did the guys make the decision because the time was now available to find a new bass player? If we'd gone straight to the US would I still be in the band? It was more than losing a gig in a band; AC/DC was a lifestyle. Life as I'd known it had ceased to exist. I was out and it hurt like hell.

I was the Sandman, or I used to be. I had developed the skill of falling asleep almost at will while in AC/DC, in cars, buses, studios and planes. Yet I sat through the entire thirty-eight-hour flight without a wink of sleep; not even the crap in-flight movies could help me nod off. Scotch wasn't touching the sides, either. I bounced between feeling desperately depressed about my sacking and deeply relieved to be out and in control of my life again.

No one outside the band knew that I was on my way to Melbourne. I was looking forward to surprising my mother. I arrived at the Hilton late on the morning of her birthday. When I knocked on the door of Club 56, she was so surprised she didn't quite comprehend that it was me, or at least that's how it seemed. A moment or two passed before she burst into tears and gave me a huge hug. Ouch! I didn't know my mother was that strong. Her hugs and tears continued for much too long; it became obvious that she was upset, very upset, the exact opposite of the effect I was hoping for.

'What's wrong?' I asked her.

'Markie,' she said, 'I didn't recognise you until you said, "Happy Birthday, Mum." You look awful.'

Chapter 11

'I'm Jewish. Tattoos are out of the question'

It was May 1977. I was back in Melbourne, on the verge of a typically bleak Victorian winter, the kind that used to make my four-year-old legs go numb. I hadn't planned on this, no way. I was all geared up to be hitting the US for the first time with AC/DC. But not only was I back in Melbourne, I was in my old bed at the Hilton, nursing a ripper of a hangover. I was staring at the corner where my bass rig used to live, the bass rig that once mocked me into action. Shit—where was my bass rig? It was in England somewhere. Great. I didn't manage to cut it in the UK, I get my arse kicked all the way back to the Hilton, but my bass rig got to stay. My hangover got worse.

In the few days since my return, I'd caught up with my family and Graham Kennedy, my old partner in crime, and that was great. Something always puzzled me about Graham: he's my best pal, we're like brothers, there was never an issue between us—but he got on famously with Angus. I'd have the occasional gripe and Graham would be straight back at me: 'What's your problem? Angus is a great bloke.' Go figure.

But now my mind had moved on to the big question: What next?

I'd come to the conclusion that it wasn't a good idea to rush back to London. Why not stick it out here in Melbourne for a bit, go to the footy, see what comes up? Bon's words were still ringing in my ears, about Australia being a step backwards, but this was the time to take stock and get my head back on straight.

What was messing with my brain was how my life had been turned upside down. I'd been cocooned by AC/DC, had my expenses taken care of, drew a weekly wage; I'd basically had my life arranged for me. I now felt isolated, with no real plan. I had no money coming in, either. The AC/DC cash I did have tucked away wasn't going to last forever.

I'd been back for less than a week when I got a distress call from a guy named Brian Todd, who managed a band called Finch. They'd supported AC/DC a few times; their guitar player Bob Spencer was the guy who supplied me with a list of questions for Paul Kossoff. Bob had moved on to another band and now their bass player had bailed.

'Can you get down to Tassie—now? Please?'

Tasmania? Oh shit, it was going to be colder than Melbourne. But I started to think it might be a good idea to help out. For one thing, their front man, Owen Orford, was a hell of a singer, and it was an earner. Tasmania, here I come.

Before too long I was a permanent member of the band, along with my pal Graham Kennedy on guitar. The line-up was completed by Barry Cram on drums and Dave Hinds on guitar. We were quickly signed to CBS Records and underwent a name change from Finch to Contraband for US releases.

Contraband spent much of its life on the road, much like AC/DC, mainly doing our own shows but also touring with stable mates Dragon, and supporting Status Quo. I met a young lady named Kobe Steele, who did PR for a number of bands, us included. Kobe also had her own TV show, a rock music program called *Right On*, pitched at the after-schoolers, which aired at 4.30 pm on weekdays. She was Sydney-based and I soon moved north to be with her.

It wasn't long before déjà vu kicked in—Contraband was doing the same pub gigs in Melbourne, Sydney, Adelaide and Brisbane that were the life blood of AC/DC and encountering some similarly hostile environments. One very memorable episode, for all the wrong reasons, was at Selina's at the Coogee Bay Hotel in Sydney. Selina's was a beachside gig, a short walk from Bon's preferred digs, the Corban Motel on Coogee Bay Road. The venue was known for having a particularly rough clientele so it wasn't unusual to see the bouncers handing out some summary justice to the punters. The clientele was rough, the bouncers were even rougher and there were plenty of both. Bobby Dunlop, the former Australian light-heavyweight boxing champion, was rumoured to help out the bouncers on occasion, so it was a brave or very pissed punter who chose to cause a kerfuffle.

We were halfway through our set on a Saturday night and a guy got up out of the crowd onto the stage to take issue with our drummer, grabbing Barry by the shoulders while he was belting the crap out of his kit, as per usual. It was my impression that the next thing to get the crap belted out of them would be this stage invader, and that was exactly what happened. Barry got off his kit and flattened him. End of argument? Unfortunately, not so. It became clear that the invader was, in fact, a bouncer who had been told to get up on stage and tell us to turn the sound down. He'd made a rather bad fist of it and at the same time met Barry's fist—and here come some more bouncers!

That was it. We downed tools and it was on for young and old between the band and the bouncers, live on stage at Selina's. We were going well. My old mate from AC/DC, Pat Pickett, and another of our crew, Terry 'the Buke' Buchanan, were firing up along with the band and it was looking like a win for the good guys. (Which was us, by the way.) That was until our erstwhile manager Brian Todd got involved. I always thought of Brian as more of a negotiator than a fighter, and he managed to negotiate a king-hit right on his nose, courtesy of a bouncer, as soon as he joined the fracas. Now if you threw a punch at Brian it would be difficult not to land one on a nose like his—it's an outstanding target. This all happened in full view of his wife Sue, who absolutely freaked; both Brian and his nose were a real mess.

Sue reacted instinctively. She was off and running to the front of the gig to get help in the form of another six-pack of bouncers. 'Quick,' she yelled, 'there are some guys beating up the band!' When I saw the bouncers charging through the crowd, I knew we were most definitely fucked.

Graham and me were off the front of the stage when the bouncers' reinforcements arrived. The punters, who had been watching and cheering us on, had started to side with us but now it had all simmered down to a stand-off, with plenty of threats, some push and shove—but with the punters ready to turn on the bouncers. That's the only thing that saved us from a monumental thrashing: the punters, and loads of them, thankfully.

Graham and I were still off the stage with Pat Pickett. Things were calming down and when I heard Graham yell something I briefly took my eyes off the bouncer in front of me. And that's the last thing I recall for a while. Pat told me later that I was on the receiving end of the biggest kick in the balls he had ever seen. He gleefully recounted that I got lifted off the ground and was out like a light by the time I hit the floor. He even gave my mother a full report the next time he saw her. Pat has always held the view that a good kick in the balls will stop any fight, as everyone else is so pleased that they didn't cop it in the nuts. Sure stopped me, that's for sure.

I carried with me a lasting memento of the Selina's gig. My nuts swelled up to what seemed like tennis balls and then proceeded to go through a number of interesting colour changes: angry blue/purple sunset by Sunday morning giving way to more pastel shades in the coming days, before fading to a jaundiced yellow. I was in a world of discomfort for weeks, walking around like I'd done some hard time on a horse. I know I was in a bad way because I didn't think about women until at least the coming mid-week.

ϟ

Contraband went into the studio with CBS house producer Peter Dawkins, who was having great international success with Air Supply and locally with Dragon, a band with loads of hits but plenty of angst due to some serious drug issues. When we were in the studio with Peter, I ought to have applied the lessons I'd learned when I was working with

George and Harry. We were a guitar band with a kick-arse front man; a loud, gutsy rock band that could knock out a decent ballad, too. We got lost trying to sound radio friendly, searching for the big hit. It's very easy now to see where we screwed up. We had a strong live following, built up through the time-honoured Aussie way of gigs and more gigs, but the recordings sounded like another band.

We had a very solid hit, 'Where Were You', off our first album, *Nothing to Hide*. It charted strongly but it wasn't all that indicative of the band live. It reminded me a little of the 'Love Song' situation with AC/DC when I first joined; it had fuck-all to do with the real band. Unfortunately for Contraband there was no 'Baby Please Don't Go' on the B-side to rescue us. I can't even remember what was on the B-side, to be honest, so it must have been a real cracker. We had managed to divide our audience: there were the faithful gig-going punters who dug us as a loud pub rock band but were stymied by the sugary 'Where Were You', and then there were our new 'fans', who were turning up to gigs expecting a load of media-friendly tunes like 'Where Were You'. Instead they encountered a bunch of yahoos, full of booze and bad manners. It got to the point where 'Where Were You' gave us all the shits and we ditched it from the set, much to the chagrin of our record company and Peter Dawkins.

In early 1978, Contraband was scheduled to spend an indefinite stretch of time in the US to record, tour and, ideally, make a fortune. Kobe and I had a chat. If we felt that what there was between us still existed when I returned, then we'd get married. It seemed perfect. At the last minute the band's US trip got boned but Kobe and I stuck to our plans and were married on the SS *Vagabond* on Sydney Harbour on

3 July 1979. Graham Kennedy, of course, was my best man. Graham always had my best interests at heart. On our way to the wharf and, hopefully, my rendezvous with wedded bliss, he turned to me and said: 'Hey, mate, we can get the cab to take us to the airport and we can fuck off.'

'Thanks, mate, but I'm good,' I replied.

It was one hell of a night. John 'Swanee' Swan was the barman and Pat Pickett was on the top deck reciting Keats and throwing the furniture into Sydney Harbour.

⚡

Contraband would spend the best part of two months on the road touring with Dragon in late 1978. Dragon were the headliners as they were stringing the hits together, mostly penned by their keyboard player, Paul Hewson. We toured the east coast from Melbourne to Far North Queensland; that's a 3000-kilometre stretch of the Australian coastline. Excuse the pun, but it's a long way.

The focal point of Dragon was their charismatic singer, Marc Hunter, a great front man and a giant of a guy, as was Marc's brother Todd, the band's bass player. If you had to draw a rock star, chances are you would end up with something that looked like Marc. Tall, slim, a great stage presence but with an acid tongue and a feel of danger around him. Dragon had something in common with Contraband; we were both being shaped as pop/rock bands, which was much to do with our recordings. Neither band saw it that way but Dragon definitely seemed to resent it a whole lot more than we did. We were prepared to play the game but Dragon railed against it. Some nights Dragon were just the most unbelievable band, great songs, hit songs, delivered with a whole lot more gusto, flair and drive than on the more tame studio stuff. But on an off night . . . holy crap, it was a different band; it looked to me like they couldn't give a fuck. They seemed to be two different bands, one amazing, the other shithouse.

We shared a tour bus, so we were living in close quarters and it became noticeable that some of the Dragon guys suffered from chronic colds. Why else would there be all these empty cough syrup bottles all over the place? They were a constant irritant to our friendly bus captain Max, who would do a clean-out each morning with a fair bit of gut-aching. When we got to a major city, no colds, no cough syrup, no mood swings, all was good with Dragon. Head out to the country and a few days later Max was grumbling all over again about the empty bottles rolling around his bus.

It was my first close-up experience of the effect of heroin. It was mystifying to me. Dragon were on a roll, the US was beckoning and these were intelligent people, but Paul, in particular, didn't seem to care about any prospects unless it revolved around getting seriously wrecked. There were times where I got on with him famously, spending late nights playing chess. He was a great player too. I managed to push him on rare occasions but I know he was cruising most of the time we got to play. We shared some great conversations, laughs too, but the other side of the guy was just plain nasty and frankly he could be an absolute arrogant prick. I should know, but Paul took the arrogant prick thing to a whole new level that was way beyond me.

We had a night off on the Gold Coast, in Surfers Paradise. We all were staying in a high-rise apartment block and I got into the lift on the eighth floor. Paul was already in the lift.

He was whacked but had a full bottle of Johnnie Walker Black with him. He made a big deal of cracking it and chugging it, didn't even blink as half the bottle went down before we got out in the lobby. We ordered cabs, waited, and before Paul got into his taxi he had finished the last of the bottle. A full bottle of Johnnie Walker in less than twenty minutes. That was the smartarse Paul, the one that gave me the shits, the same guy who was great company playing chess one night but the next an arsehole who would not even say hello to me in a lift—or offer me a pull on his bottle of Johnnie.

It all came to a head with Paul after a record reception in Melbourne for the release of their single 'April Sun in Cuba'. We had all hit the turps at the reception and Paul was being the rock star, which I guess is par for the course at a record reception for your band. Paul had been sniping away at me but once we got to a party later at a friend's place, it all got too much. Paul was telling me how he had never met a bass player that he liked, which was dumb as his bass player, Todd, a monster of a man, was standing right next to me. He also went on to declare that the Doors were his all-time favourite band because 'they didn't have a slimy fuckin' bass player'. That was it for me. I headbutted him and he went flying over a coffee table. I followed and started punching the crap out of him. I completely lost it. I was drunk but frustrated out of my mind by Paul. Why was he such a fuckin' arsehole?

The next thing I knew I was flying backwards. Todd had grabbed me by the shoulders and reefed me off Paul, thankfully. At that point I thought Todd was about to rip my head off, but much to his credit, he did nothing but restore some peace and sanity. It was bad enough that I bashed Paul but I did it in front of a whole bunch of CBS people, including

Peter Dawkins and Lorne Saifer, who was the head of our US label, Portrait. Not a great career move.

ϟ

Contraband was booked to play a big outdoor show on the forecourt of the Sydney Opera House, supporting the Little River Band. This was a big deal; the anticipated crowd was 30,000 plus, and we were hoping this gig would finally break us in Sydney, after a couple of half hits. The major rock radio station in Sydney, 2SM, was sponsoring the show—the same station that banned AC/DC until we made it clear that we were musicians, not strippers.

Bon was in town so I invited him along and we were to pick him up at his place, the Corban Motel. I knocked on his door; he was ready to go but invited me in.

'I have something for you, mate,' he said. 'We all got given these in New York. I got another one for you; you should have got one anyway.'

On first look, he handed me what appeared to be a gold Cartier watch, the slightly rectangular-faced model with Roman numerals and a black band. I looked a little more closely. Instead of saying 'Cartier' it read: 'Atlantic Records.' Looks like they'd learned to love AC/DC.

Bon gave me his big trademark grin when he saw I was pleased and more than a little moved by his thoughtfulness. He was that kind of guy, generous to a fault, caring. Until he got legless, of course. At that point it all went out the window.

'Let's have a belt before we go,' Bon offered. How could I say no?

The Opera House forecourt was packed when we arrived.

It was a beautiful Sydney day by the harbour and I was charged up, thanks to Bon. We were the second band of four on the bill and we were firing, getting a great reaction. There was plenty of noise, the type of volume that can only come from a big outdoor crowd. Bon had a good viewing spot, behind the PA on my side of the stage, crouched down next to his best mate Pat Pickett, who was my stage roadie. On the other side was Pat's backup, Frazer Young, Mal and Angus's nephew. Frazer's brother Steve would fill in for Mal when he took some time off the road from AC/DC.

The gig went extra well. Afterwards, I was keen to get Bon's take on the band.

'Singer is great,' he began. 'But it's not loud enough and piss the slow songs off, fucks your direction up. It's a rock band, isn't it? Forget the slow stuff, mate. Fancy another belt, Mark?'

Fuck I missed this guy.

While I was trying to get things rolling with Contraband, Rose Tattoo was also brewing up. They'd been signed to Alberts after Bon championed their cause to George and Harry. Angry Anderson, the Tatts singer, was an old bandmate of Phil's from Melbourne. The Tatts are my all-time favourite group; no other country in the world could produce a band like these guys. They were the ultimate Aussie rock act.

Their original bass player, Ian Rilen, had decided to move on early in the piece. Mick Cocks was filling in on bass, itching to get back into his rightful place of the Tatts' rhythm guitar player. He told me he hated playing bass—would I consider joining? But the tattoo issue was a hitch. I was terrified of them. Didn't want one.

'Sorry, they're a must-have,' I was told by their manager, Mick Christian.

'Can't do it,' I replied. 'I'm Jewish. Tattoos are out of the question.'

The Jewish thing has followed me around ever since.

Frankly, I would have joined Rose Tattoo like a shot if I hadn't committed to Contraband. If an offer had come earlier I wouldn't have been able to say yes fast enough. Still, it kickstarted a lifelong friendship with Mick Cocks, a fellow Carlton supporter, and our paths would be intertwined from that point on.

Contraband eventually ran out of gas. We shelved it for a while, or so we thought, but in the end it just stayed there, on the shelf. In 1981, I joined up with guitar player Robin Riley and drummer John 'JL' Lalor to form the Beast. The Beast was renowned for two things: its sheer volume and the stinking overalls that Robin wore on stage. They were so nasty that the road crew refused to carry them. Rob's overalls travelled from gig to gig tied to the bullbar on the front of the truck.

The Beast was Robin's band, there could be no other way because Rockin' Rob is simply larger than life, just like his monumental guitar playing. He is a massive bear of a man, a real beer-swilling Aussie character with an incredible presence; he can look truly frightening on stage, practically psychotic, sometimes comical, and I have always thought that he would make a perfect cartoon character as he is halfway there already with his impressive selection of tattoos. Rob has been known to act like a real buffoon, mostly on stage, but that belies the fact that he writes great rock songs and can even knock out a real country-style tearjerker. On the inside he is an absolute teddy bear, a real sweetheart. Sorry, Rob, but that's the truth and you know it even though you can look like an axe murderer. Then there is the ear-shattering volume that he plays at; no one does guitar volume like Rob. It might have a lot to do with the fact that he wears two hearing aids, although I'm not sure what actually came first, the volume or the hearing aids.

Rob's unkempt appearance can be disconcerting and at times he has had scant regard for personal hygiene, a point that rankled with the Beast's PA guy/manager Tony Malouf. Tony was a tiny, hyperactive Mr Clean of Lebanese extraction and he and Rob certainly made an odd-looking duo, a wild-eyed manic little dynamo and a sloth-like, shambolic mountain of a man, but they buddied up big time, which may have a lot to do with the massive joints Tony would roll. One masterpiece was over a foot long and kicked like a mule. I watched them smoke it in a hotel room in Tweed Heads. Rob ended up lying on the floor, asking me, 'Hey, mate, am I still here?' Never got involved with their dope smoking myself, but I can't imagine what Tony would have been like if he hadn't been whacked out of his mind. We would have had to peel him off the ceiling.

Tony was an obsessive clean freak, and he caught on very early that Rob could be more than a tad messy, so when Tony's Volvo was needed to transport the band he would spend the afternoon lining the complete interior of his car with clear plastic sheets to Riley-proof it. Rob took this as a personal challenge on a ninety-minute drive from Sydney to Terrigal and let loose with a constant barrage of thermo-nuclear farts that Tony did not acknowledge once, which took some doing as JL and I were ready to throw up. We would learn later that Tony had no sense of smell. Lucky prick.

As if by destiny, we were headed for Alberts. We spent many hours putting down demo tracks, along with a lot of beer, with Sam Horsborough, the nephew of George, Mal and Angus. We were building up a fine stock of tunes that George would review and critique. We were on our way to doing an album and feeling mighty good about it as we were building up a strong following in the Sydney pubs and clubs. It was looking good for the Beast.

Rose Tattoo, meanwhile, had moved to England, where they were making serious waves. But trouble was brewing in the ranks. Mick Cocks was on his way out and who did the Tatts want to replace Mick? Robin Riley. Shit! JL and I knew there was something up when one part of Rose Tattoo's management, Sam Righi, turned up at a Beast gig at the Caringbah Hotel and hijacked Rob after the show. The ironic part of the deal was that Sam Righi and Mick Cocks were very close—but this was business and an opportunity too good for Rob to pass up. Bye-bye, Rob. Bye-bye, Beast.

I have been asked many times who is the best guitar player I have worked with. Most expect me to answer either Malcolm or Angus Young, naturally, as both those guys are in a class of their own, but my immediate answer is always 'Robin Riley'. Rockin' Rob is just an unbelievable player, heaps of soul, intensity and always hits the right note—maybe only one note, but you are guaranteed it will be a killer. Rob could pull a great tone out of a baseball bat and he deserves a whole lot more recognition and success than has come his way.

ϟ

In February 1981, I was at the Sydney Showgrounds, sitting in a viewing area set aside for family and friends, watching AC/DC rip through their homecoming gig, their first

Australian show since June 1977. All the usual shortcomings of a large outdoor venue like the Showground couldn't derail the band or the crowd. After all, this was a special occasion: AC/DC was in Sydney, the town that thought of itself as the band's spiritual home.

Apart from that one short set as a four-piece at the Station Hotel way back in March 1975, this was the first time I'd actually seen the band without being part of it. Yet I was feeling detached; the guys were playing great, but I wasn't with them—and neither was Bon . . .

By early 1980 I was settling into married life with my wife, Kobe. We lived in Randwick, one of Sydney's eastern suburbs, famous for its racecourse. One afternoon I was taking it easy at home, reading. I was stretched out on our very comfortable couch when the phone rang. It was my good friend Brian Todd, who managed Contraband.

'Hi Mark. I'm just down the road, I have a bottle of Scotch, I'll see you in a few minutes.'

This was odd. Brian lived way across town and was not apt to just drop in.

'What's up, mate?' I asked.

After a long pause, Brian, said, 'You haven't been watching TV?'

What sort of fuckin' stupid question was that?

'Bon's dead.'

Shit . . . no . . . 'Are you sure?'

'He's gone, mate. It's all over the TV and radio. He was in London. See you in a bit.'

No. Not now. I had to sit down; I felt like I was going to pass out. I fell onto the same couch that Bon had passed out on the last time he was here.

'I want to do a solo album,' Bon had said that night, 'like Lynyrd Skynyrd kind of stuff, but real ballsy, something that swings.'

He was pissed and so was I but it was always great to catch up with Bon. It was strange; since I left the band I'd become closer to Bon. I had spent some great nights out with him and Silver, so maybe he felt he could talk more openly with me about the problems he was having. He loved staying near the beach and planted himself at the Corban Motel, only a five-minute walk from my place in Randwick, so it wasn't unusual for him to drop over in the period after I left the band. If I was out Bon would leave a bottle of Scotch on my doorstep, his calling card, a sign that he'd be coming back. These days it was more likely to be a bottle of Jack Daniels but who the fuck cared what it was? Bon was in town.

'Yep, a swingin' loud and nasty solo album, real down-home stuff,' Bon had told me, between swigs. 'Gotta record it in the States, though. Got some good boys in mind, too.'

Bon was flying; he had a new motorbike and had been charging round town full of goodness knows what. It seemed as though the memories and the pain of his near-fatal bike accident in Adelaide in '74 had receded, but the more likely scenario was that Bon was being Bon. Fuck tomorrow, it's today; tomorrow can look after itself. Pass the Jack Daniels and let's do another line. That was Bon.

'Mate,' I said to him, 'that's going to be an interesting band meeting when you tell the guys about what you want to do.'

Bon flashed me one of his big, cheeky grins. 'I'll let you know how I go . . .'

'Mark! Open the door!'

Shit. Brian. I got up, let Brian in and plonked straight back on the couch. I had no legs, I felt heavy, like I'd been knocked out and I was just coming to. This can't be happening, not now, the guys are just starting to break big, not fuckin' now.

'Scotch, mate?' Brian asked. 'I'm so sorry, I called as soon as I heard. I was just down the road—I thought you would have known already.'

I felt numb. Brian was talking but I couldn't make sense of what he was saying. I thought he said something about a car . . .

'Was it a car accident?' I asked him.

'No,' Brian answered. 'They found him in a car.'

My mind flashed back to the number of times I'd seen Bon pissed and passed out in the back seat of a car, head flopping forward as we sped home from a gig with low-flyin' Phil at the wheel. Bon's breathing would get wheezy—just how hard would it be for him to wake up and get out of the car if he was seriously shellacked?

Brian's Scotch wasn't touching the sides. Here I was on the same couch, downing Scotch like I had with Bon, but no more. I was still thinking about that last time with him . . .

'I can't believe it,' Bon had said to me. 'You've been on that couch for more than ten minutes and you're still awake. Fuck, you've changed, Mark.'

'No, I'm the still the same,' I assured him. 'I can fall asleep anywhere. You're the one keeping me awake, arsehole.' He was the same Bon, only he was looking tired, drinking more and he was still lonely, missing Silver and not quite knowing where the relationship was at. I reckoned it was down the gurgler—he hoped it wasn't.

The day after Bon's death I walked into Fifa's office at Boomerang House. As soon as I saw her it all closed in on me.

I knew Bon was gone but whatever piece was missing clicked when I saw Fifa. We didn't have to say a word. What could be said that meant anything, anyway?

As I was leaving, Narelle, Fifa's assistant, called out to me. 'Mark! *Highway to Hell* went gold in the US last Monday.'

'Thanks, Narelle,' I said, managing a smile. 'So fuckin' what,' I thought.

'IN THE BEGINNING . . .' The crowd went ballistic, pulling me back from my thoughts. They were roaring at Bon's famous introductory sermon from 'Let There Be Rock'. They were Bon's words, sure enough, but Brian Johnson was delivering them to a packed Sydney Showground and the crowd was eating it up. AC/DC were back in Sydney, alive and kicking.

I had trouble a few times during the show with my emotions. It was just an unbelievable experience. I'd hear the band hit an intro I had played hundreds of times before, but when the vocals started, it wasn't Bon. That really jarred me. I should have been prepared for it, but I wasn't. Thankfully I was in a relatively private area, with people that knew me well, so they cut me a bit of slack.

After the show, family, friends and invited guests—me and Kobe included—made our way to a massive marquee in the backstage area to celebrate the band's 'homecoming'. The vibe was fantastic; the band had just blown everyone away. All the pre-show tension about how Brian would be received had been shattered by the gig. The thousands who were at the Sydney Showground were ready to sign the papers and adopt the guy.

I'll admit it was tough for me, watching the band rip it up, but that was nothing compared to what the guys were working their way through. They'd endured plenty to get to this point. You had to respect that sort of resolve.

I caught up with the guys for a chat and a few laughs. We were presented with loads of gold and platinum records and a speech by Ted Albert really hit the spot. There was one awkward moment, though, when some mug heckler piped up with: 'Where's the real band?' Pat Pickett stood up, pointed at the heckler and said, 'Shut your mouth or I will shit in it.' Ted was a little taken aback but then added: 'I wish I had said that.' It was a priceless moment. Bon's mate had let everybody know where he stood.

There were loads of photos taken with Ted and Fifa. It was an unusual AC/DC line-up—just for a moment there were two bass players, Cliff Williams and myself. Still, it was warming to be so welcomed by the guys and the Alberts crew. It was a great night, a triumph for AC/DC. It was also the last civil contact I'd have with the band.

Michael Browning stepped back into my life suddenly. Michael had parted ways with AC/DC and was now managing a band called Heaven, who were in the US. Michael put in a distress call to me.

'Can you and JL come over to LA and join the band?'

'Sure. Sounds good.'

'By the way, you'll be on rhythm guitar. We want you to replace Mick Cocks.'

Shit!

Mick, bless him, was cool about it. He'd had enough of butting heads with the singer, yet another Glaswegian, a guy named Allen Fryer. Allen had been widely tipped to be the singer to replace Bon in AC/DC; it was even reported as a done deal in *Melody Maker*.

Mick had palled up with Bon when he was in England with Rose Tattoo. It got to the stage where Mick became his road buddy, sharing a hotel suite, a seat on the tour bus and generally hanging out with Bon. In London, Mick was moving in circles that included Silver, now Bon's ex, and her friend Joe Furey, who'd been with Silver at the hospital on the night Bon died.

'I didn't know Bon was toff!' Mick told me. 'He used to like it when I called him that when he ordered a nice red with dinner.'

I could see why Bon and Mick hit it off so well; they were very similar guys who really knew how to enjoy themselves. It would have been like watching a doped-up Laurel and Hardy in action.

One morning, Mick was on the AC/DC bus when a crew member summoned him to the back to speak with Mal. Mal grilled Mick about his friendship with Bon. To quote Mick, 'I thought I was going to be asked what my intentions were.'

JL and I landed in LA and hit the road almost immediately with Heaven, who were supporting Mötley Crüe on their Shout at the Devil tour. I'd been forewarned about how tough touring with these guys could be. 'Okay,' I thought, 'I'll watch myself.' Ready for anything, I was confronted by a bunch of dudes in high heels and make-up. What the fuck was all this? Once I got past the lippy and heels, they were cool guys, particularly the singer Vince Neil and Tommy Lee, the drummer. But hard-arses? You've got to be kidding! I'd say someone's PR person was hitting the pipe a bit hard.

Early in the tour we got snowbound in Denver, Colorado, and were stuck in our hotel for three days. We escaped one night to a bar across the street called Johnny's, run by a massive cowboy—named Johnny, strangely enough. He was loud, abrasive and a real pain in the backside. He thought he was the best pool player in Denver and told anyone who'd listen that he'd play them for fifty bucks a game.

That's my kind of talk! Rack 'em up, cowboy!

I couldn't believe it; he couldn't miss. He kept getting all the breaks and I was getting jack shit. I lost four games on the trot. I was down $200, out of cash—and I was filthy. Johnny didn't help by telling the world about it.

'Hey, I thought you Aussies could play pool. No way! Ha ha!'

He was driving me crazy.

'Hey,' he snorted, 'how about one more game for a hundred bucks? But seeing that you don't have any money, when I win you give me all your clothes. Then you go back home in the snow butt naked. Deal?'

'Rack 'em up, Johnny.'

Laurie Marlow, Heaven's bass player, told me I was crazy. I was, but I wanted to beat this arsehole so badly. A crowd had built up, some side betting had kicked in. I heard a call: 'Kick his fat butt all over Colorado!'

The table turned my way from the very next game. I wasn't going out naked into the snow. We kept playing, the bar shut, we kept playing, he kept losing and Johnny started getting very steamed up. The drinks kept coming and now I couldn't miss. This was more like it. Johnny started to accuse me of hustling him after I potted two off the break and then cleared the table. He didn't get a shot and had to hand over another hundred.

Johnny went to the till a few times for cash until I'd cleaned him of the night's takings, a shade over $2000. The fat fucker still owes me $500.

Our next tour was supporting Kiss, the same outfit I'd chuckled at back in London. It was their 'controversial' Unmasked tour, which they did without make-up. Bad move, guys. It didn't take long to figure out why they'd been caking on the greasepaint. They were butt ugly. Gene Simmons, however, was an interesting fellow, a larger-than-life character not shy about handing out advice.

'Hey, I'm a big fan of you guys,' he told us one night. 'I want to produce your next record.'

Heaven had half a hit going at the time, a song called 'Rock School' that was featuring heavily on the fledgling MTV. It was looking good. We were doing a photo shoot for a Japanese magazine at the back door of the ice hockey stadium where we were playing that night. The back door opened and Gene was in the middle of his own photo shoot with that tongue of his on full display—*eeeccchhh*. Then he started talking fluent Japanese with the photographer, cracking jokes. At least I guess he was cracking jokes, because they were pissing themselves laughing. Maybe the joke was on Heaven. Gene didn't end up getting into the studio with us.

We followed up the Unmasked tour with some dates supporting Black Sabbath. No, not again! The line-up had changed. Ozzy was gone and Ian Gillan from Deep Purple was on vocals, with Tony Iommi on guitar, Bev Bevan on drums and Geezer Butler, Malcolm Young's sparring partner, still on bass. This tour was famous for one thing: they used Stonehenge as their stage setting. Anyone who's seen *Spinal Tap* will know what I'm talking about. Fucking Stonehenge!

The men of Sabbath would emerge through these big fake stones (they weren't even real fake), amid dry ice and spooky music. It was a fuckin' howler. I couldn't help myself; I had to round up a cheer squad for Geezer's bass solo, just like we'd done in AC/DC. We were geed up, standing at the side of the stage, ready for his first clanger. Away Geezer went and . . . wait for it . . . YES! A big cheer went up and Geezer's head shot around. I couldn't help but notice he had a surprised but slightly haunted look on his face. He'd heard that cheer before. But where? And when? Fucking Aussies.

Heaven imploded during an Australian tour in 1984, so I found myself back in Sydney, sharing a house with Graham Kennedy and my girlfriend Bille, once again pondering what was next. My marriage hadn't lasted. I was to blame for that, but what did come of our union was a beautiful daughter, Kristin, who was born in Perth on 25 February 1982. Early on, I didn't see much of Kristin at all, until she and Kobe came back to live in Sydney. We ironed out some issues and I became a weekend dad—or at least an every-second-weekend dad. I was a very proud and happy one at that.

Dave Tice was the singer in Australia's prime heavy metal band, Buffalo. He formed the band with his best mate Pete Wells in the early 1970s. They went on to tour endlessly like all good bands did in those days and recorded four landmark heavy metal albums for the prestigious Vertigo label, the home of Black Sabbath. Pete would go on to form Rose Tattoo. Dave would eventually take off to England to front the Count Bishops.

Dave was back in Sydney by the mid-1980s, busy (well, sort of, anyway) putting together a band that was to be called the Headhunters. He was looking to change bass players and I was fingered as a replacement to join Greg Skehill on drums and Mick Cocks (yep, him again) on guitar. Coincidentally I would be replacing Joe Furey, Silver Smith's friend, who had relocated to Sydney. The Headhunters were a bar band, based at the Royal Hotel just a few hundred metres up the hill from the iconic Bondi Beach.

The Headhunters and the Royal Hotel were a great double. Sunday afternoons there became an institution and some interesting guests, including Pat Cash, the Wimbledon and Davis Cup-winning tennis player, who'd become a firm friend, would join us. Pat was also an apprentice rock guitarist. Mick and I would play tennis with Pat and Pat would play guitar with us. It was the perfect contra deal; Mick and I would be inducted into the Pat Cash Band, too. Mick and I would be called in to put the band together for Pat with singers Juno Roxas and Spencer Jones and drummer Mick O'Shea. Mick Cocks's pal Sam Righi, along with Michael Browning, managed the whole deal so it had a real family feel to it, although I certainly could have done without playing a couple of Bryan Adams tunes in the set.

The Royal Hotel had other dividends. It introduced Mick and me to the East Sydney Bulldogs. East Sydney was the local team in the Sydney Football League and Mick and I pulled the boots on for a season of Australian Rules football. We got through pre-season training, but only just. On the first night we turned up, the players headed off on a ten-kilometre road run, Mick and I tailing behind them, puffing and panting like a couple of old rockers. When we regained our breath we got to meet a great bunch of guys—Bomber, Marsh, Jimmy O, Muscles, Bananas, Rick M and PC. The Headhunters became house band at the East Sydney Bulldogs Club, which doubled as the HQ for the Sydney Swans, one of twelve teams in what was then the Victorian Football League.

Mick almost made it through the season until he did his knee during the second last match. I got to the last training session before doing my knee in and missing the final game. I had my knee surgically reconstructed, while Mick chose to complain a lot about his but dodge the reco. So ended our stellar football careers but the Headhunters marched on, except for Mick, who limped a bit.

Bille and I decided to get married, but rather than go through all the rigmarole planning a wedding we decided to elope to Las Vegas. In Vegas I met up with our good pal Wayne Marshall, a US-based Australian tennis coach, and headed off on the bucks' night. We decided to let Bille tag along, too. We all got nicely smashed and were ferried around town by a delightful Jamaican cab driver named Randall who informed us that a certain multinational fast food chain in Australia used kangaroo meat in their burgers. Thanks, Randall.

It was 105 degrees in Vegas on our wedding day, 3 August 1991. I was hungover, sweating bullets in our suite at the Flamingo Hilton. I decided that the perfect hangover cure would be a bottle of Dom Perignon. Yep, that worked. That much done, I figured that another would work twice as well. Clark County Court House was looking hazy (maybe it was the heat) but we got our marriage certificate and were pointed in the direction of the Gracelands Wedding Chapel—and guess who?

We were getting checked in by a three-hundred-pound Bubba at Gracelands, when Wayne was asked to sign the documents.

'Sign here, Dwayne.'

'It's Wayne, by the way.'

Bubba was getting agitated, sweating freely. He gestured to Wayne. 'Shove over, Dwayne!'

Huh?

'I got two hundred on the Yankees. Move over, man, I can't see the game!'

Bubba was watching the baseball on the TV in the corner while we were 'all fixed up to get married'. Only in Vegas.

Bubba offered Bille the plastic flowers they provided but she had thoughtfully bought her own bouquet at the Flamingo. Reverend Harrison was waiting for us in the chapel and introduced Elvis to sing a song or two before the ceremony began. I was gone, as nervous as hell, when Elvis asked me: 'Well, sir, what would y'all like to hear on your wedding day?'

I was blank. Here I was, toasted and toasting in Vegas, getting married, and the King had asked me which one of his songs I wanted to hear. And I had nothing. Zip.

'Hey, Dwayne,' I said—it was catching—'give me an Elvis song, pleeease!'

'I really like that one: "I'm caught in a trap, I can't go on".'

And that's how 'Suspicious Minds' became our wedding song.

We went on a six-week honeymoon that took in LA, the rest of Vegas, San Francisco and New York, and then we headed over to the UK to meet up with Pat Cash and his wife Emily. Bille has always ribbed me that I can't go anywhere without meeting someone I know, and we walked into Browns in London with Pat and Emily when a bloke walked straight up and gave me a huge hug. Bille gave me her usual bemused 'not this again' look and I introduced her to Ian Jeffrey, AC/DC's former front-of-house sound guy. I hadn't seen him for fourteen years. It was drinks all round and a big night. Ian was tour managing Metallica and arranged for us to go see them play the Monsters of Rock festival at Donington, along with the Black Crowes, Mötley Crüe and, yep, AC/DC. Nice.

It was an icy cold and windswept day at Donington. We completely missed the Black Crowes, but caught a bit of Mötley Crüe. All the typical Crüe hootin' and hollerin' was going on, although the leather gear, ripped T-shirts, high heels and make-up seemed more than a tad out of place, especially in the daylight. They were the perfect rock and roll parody.

It was the bank holiday weekend in England, the middle of summer, and here I was freezing my nuts off on the side of the stage while Metallica blazed away. This was summer? I got so cold I was forced to hit the merchandise stand and buy a Mötley Crüe sweatshirt to try to keep warm. Why Mötley Crüe? They were the only ones left.

Metallica was on fire. Their style of music is a tad on the heavy side for me but these guys knocked me out with their intensity. There was some very sharp playing going on, too; they sounded to me like a band at the very top of their game. Supporting AC/DC would seem to be a thankless task, but Metallica were giving it plenty, ripping right into it, and the punters were eating it up.

I was side stage again with Pat when he introduced me to one of the real characters of the music business, Alan Rogan. Alan is *the* guitar tech, who's worked with George Harrison,

Pete Townshend, Keith Richards, Eric Clapton and John Fogerty, among others. This guy was a legend and a vintage guitar and bass authority, a small, portly, grey-haired fellow, who spoke in a broad, almost comical English accent.

'Ahhhh, Mark Evans is it, eh? I've heard a lot about you. I work for Angus, the little fuckin' cooont.'

Alan proved to be a very handy man to know; he fetched a bunch of my gold and platinum records from the AC/DC 'lockup', as he called it, and brought them back to Australia. I'd donate those records to charities that'd use them as fundraisers.

AC/DC were the Monsters of Rock headliners. I was looking forward to seeing the band play but certainly didn't harbour any thoughts of catching up with any of the guys. Phil had been sacked and it'd been ten years since we'd all met up at the Sydney Showgrounds. Any contact since then had been purely via lawyers. The problems were associated with my separation from Alberts. I'm not legally permitted to go into the details because of a confidentiality clause attached to the out-of-court settlement that finally resolved the matter. Suffice to say the lawsuit ended the relationship with Alberts and the band. I felt that it was purely a business situation that could have been handled in a manner that didn't require teams of lawyers. Unfortunately that's not what transpired.

Maybe I was naive at the outset, but the experience of a long legal battle cured me of any lingering naivety. It was very instructional, too. If I learned anything, it was never to sign documents without the best possible legal advice available. I still wonder what I was thinking way back at the end of my time with the band, if I was thinking at all, signing documents without advice. I fully accept that I was to blame for the legal situation I found myself in. I was out of my mind to sign the document that was put in front of me. (I'd be very pleased to shake hands and put all the legal stuff into the past now the matter is resolved, but I don't hold much hope on that one.)

AC/DC opened with 'Thunderstruck' and the punters went berserk. It was a hell of a show, or at least what I saw of it. I was almost frozen solid and had to head off for some backstage warmth with Metallica and crew. AC/DC sounded extra large and loud; outdoors shows aren't usually the best venues for sound but this wasn't the case at Donington. It was powering. But I missed hearing Phil on drums; it was like taking Charlie Watts out of the Stones. Drummers have their own personal style and feel and none more so than Phil. It's something I'm stuck with; when I hear AC/DC, in my head it's with Bon and Phil on board. Still, what was important was the punters at Donington were peaking and the band was absolutely killing it.

ϟ

Playing live was starting to take a back seat for me, replaced by my passion for vintage guitars and basses. After I finished with the Headhunters I linked up with Steve Jackson, a certifiable vintage guitar nut, who ran a Sydney store called Jacksons Rare Guitars. Steve is also a Holden fanatic; he has a barn full of them. Guitars and basses I understand—but cars? I have never knowingly driven a car in my life, although I was told by Robin Riley that I once drove our band back to the hotel in Queensland after a gig, although I was too drunk to remember.

The more I learned about the vintage guitar business, the more I enjoyed it. I became associated with Steve at his store, which dealt in incredible vintage pieces that seemed to be gaining in value overnight: 1950s and 60s Fenders, Gibsons, Gretschs and Rickenbackers were the ones that got me going, along with the great acoustics from C.F. Martin & Co.

For the first time in my life I felt settled. Bille and I bought a house in Balmain, a harbourside suburb in Sydney's inner west; the vintage business was good and Kristin was growing up beautifully, much to her mother's credit. Kristin would spend every second weekend with us at Balmain and we'd have a ball. We lived on the side of a hill, our century-old terrace house was spread over three floors, with a cave-like but very cosy bar under the house. Kristin loved the bar. Come to think of it, I was pretty crazy about it too. You reached the bar via an outside spiral staircase that claimed many victims over the years. Pat Cash was so plastered one night that he actually fell up the staircase.

A by-product of the vintage guitar business was meeting and listening to amazing players and getting acquainted with some fascinating, guitar-obsessed characters. Ian Jeffrey came to Sydney, still on the same tour with Metallica, and brought Kirk Hammett and Jason Newstead from the band to the store. We did some vintage guitar business and Jason convinced me to let him have my 1968 Telecaster bass in a paisley finish. The bass was used on the Doors track 'LA Woman' and much of the *Morrison Hotel* album. I still can't believe I let it go. (Jason, I want it back!)

Bille, Kristin and I went to a Metallica gig at the Sydney Entertainment Centre. Kristin was given her own dressing room backstage and was treated like a princess (of course), even though she was possibly the only person to fall asleep during a Metallica gig. She had a serious crush on Lars the drummer. I withstood the urge to give her up and embarrass the crap out of her, but it was hard. It's a dad's right to embarrass his teenage daughter whenever possible. Lars had some background with Pat Cash: Lars was a champion junior tennis player until music sidetracked a promising sporting future.

Via the store I also met Richie Sambora from Bon Jovi. This guy was not only a killer guitar player but a gentleman to boot. On his first visit to the store he plugged a beautiful early-sixties Fender Stratocaster into a sweet 1950s Fender Champ. It's a tiny tweed amp but you can get the little critters to rip, which Richie proceeded to do. He was wailing, playing some incredible stuff; we were so engrossed that none of us noticed the amp wasn't all that pleased. Smoke started belching out the back of the thing. Richie had killed our prize amplifier! The Champ had helped us find new homes for many fine guitars but now it was dead on the floor, farting its last puff of smoke. Richie was mortified; I have never heard anyone so apologetic in my life. He insisted on paying for the amp. We refused, of course, but how I loved, and missed, that amp.

Piers Crocker, a guitar repair genius, was our next-store neighbour. One morning he alerted us that George Harrison was on his way to the store. A Beatle! What the fuck do you say to a Beatle? Particularly Harrison, who had a rep for being somewhat prickly. I wasn't exactly panicking, well maybe a little, but Steve, being a card-carrying Beatles nut, looked like he was about to explode.

George's car pulled up out front. He came to our door, which was always locked, so I let him in.

'Hello, George, thanks for coming over, please come in. Would your driver like to come in?'

George answered briskly, 'All he's done is ask questions about the Beatles ever since I got into the car. I don't care if he fuckin' starves out there.'

We were off to a flying start!

George made himself at home; he even made himself a cup of tea and settled in, playing a few guitars. It was a sensationally odd feeling sitting down and chatting with a guy like George Harrison; he's someone who I felt I have known for most of my life, although I didn't let on I was more of a Stones man. I looked him up and down and figured that someone stretched him for his Beatles bio. I recall it said he was five foot eleven, but he seemed a few inches shy of that mark. How about that? My mate Derek Taylor, the Beatles' publicist, gilding the lily!

The ice was well and truly broken and we were enjoying ourselves when Steve gestured to a Beatles poster on the back room wall.

'You remember those guys, George?'

'This could be interesting,' I thought, 'one way or another.'

'Yes, I remember that photo,' George replied. 'It was taken at a rehearsal for a TV show in London. I was late. That's why the other chaps are in their suits and I'm in my civvies.'

Phew.

George really started to open up, discussing old guitars, particularly two Sonic Blue Fender Stratocasters that he and John Lennon had bought in New York. He gave his a homemade psychedelic paint job with fluoro paint.

'It was a daft thing to do,' George confessed.

He spoke of Lennon in the present tense, even though

John had been dead for some years. It was obvious that he revered Lennon, but added that 'John can be a bit of a handful at times'. When Ringo Starr's name came up, he referred to him as Ritchie, his actual Christian name. He called Paul McCartney 'the bass player'; make of that what you will.

George started to pick out a few Beatles bits and pieces, including the barre-chord intro to 'I Feel Fine'. I looked at Steve, who I thought might pass out. George started playing the opening to 'Norwegian Wood', a stunning guitar piece. Then he sang the lilting lyric, 'I once had a girl, or should I say, she once had me.' At this point *I* thought I was going to pass out. His voice was as clear as a bell, soulful with great warmth. I didn't know he was such a fine singer, but then again he didn't get much of a crack with Lennon and McCartney to contend with. He finished his bit of 'Norwegian Wood' and told us: 'That's one of John's tunes. It's a beautiful number.' No shit, George.

As things wound up, we asked George for his mailing address so we could get information to him directly when necessary. He happily obliged.

George Harrison
Friar Park
England

'Will our stuff get to you at this address, George?' I asked him.

'Yes, of course. I have mail delivered to me addressed to "George Harrison, England".'

I thought only Santa Claus had that kind of pull.

Chapter 12

'It's a long way from Kogarah, Clive'

The thirtieth of January 1997 was a banner day for the Evans clan. We welcomed the arrival of Virginia, a beautiful daughter for Bille and myself and a little sister for Kristin. I was chuffed that an Evans had been born in Sydney, only a few hundred metres from the site where my father was born at 32 Underwood Street, Paddington, in 1916. Life was good. Very, very good.

Dave Tice and Mick Cocks had come up with the idea of a blues-based acoustic duo, to play some dates at the Tea Gardens Hotel in Bondi Junction. They'd sometimes be joined by Mick's former Rose Tattoo bandmate, Ian Rilen. I was thrown into the deep end of this mix on a Friday afternoon, not long after Virginia was born.

Mick had been talking with a friend, Karen, an ex hotel-licensee, who was opening a restaurant in Sydney's Woolloomooloo and she wanted Dave and Mick to supply the music. Two things were odd here: Karen is an Anglo/

Aussie who was opening a Chinese restaurant; and she firmly believed that acoustic blues went well with Chinese food. She called me as she couldn't locate Mick anywhere (no surprises there) or Dave, and was becoming concerned about just who'd be bringing the blues at the restaurant's opening, some four hours away.

So that's how the duo of Dave Tice and Mark Evans came into being, at the Amazing Wok in Woolloomooloo. It came as no surprise that the Chinese restaurant with bluesy overtones bought the ranch pretty quickly; it was equally surprising that from such a unique but very tasty beginning our duo thrived. I'd been playing the rare gig with the Dave Tice Band when he was short a bass player, but the duo really got me back into playing live. It wasn't long before we were offered a couple of residencies, at the Bridge Hotel in Rozelle—owned by a good mate, Richard Keough—and the Iguana Bar in Kings Cross.

Until then I didn't realise how much I missed playing. It helped that I was playing with Dave, who has an absolute monster of a voice. Our blues-based acoustic style developed from gig to gig. There is an obvious advantage of working in a duo: there can be only two points of view. If there's a difference of opinion, it had to come from the source and not be filtered through other band members. It's a very pure way to operate. What also helped make our duo run smoothly was that the Tice and Evans clans were close knit. Dave's wife Lesley was Bille's closest friend, and his daughter Savannah and our girl Virginia were tight, so there was much spirited discussion over just who was the real 'Tice & Evans'.

There were quite a few changes going on behind the scenes, too. We'd bought a new family home in Lilyfield (our home was new to us, but the house itself was over 120 years old); I was back to playing, albeit packing a Gibson J 200 acoustic guitar and not a Fender Precision Bass; Ginnie was growing and constantly smiling; Kristin had moved to the Gold Coast—and I'd found a new place of business for the vintage guitar stuff with Carlo Bova and the crew at Downtown Music. Life was rosy. What could possibly go wrong?

Kristin was nearing her eighteenth birthday. She'd moved north with her mother, Kobe, to enjoy the sun and relaxed lifestyle that the Gold Coast offered in spades. One day she'd complained of feeling unwell. The family doctor diagnosed glandular fever, which wasn't much fun for a very-soon-to-be-eighteen-year-old, but with rest she'd soon be on the mend. In theory. I spoke to her on the phone over the next week and it was obvious she wasn't on the mend at all; she said she felt like crap. Kobe was watching over Kristin as only a mother can, but with growing concern.

Kristin visited her family doctor, who was alarmed by her deteriorating condition and rushed her to the Pindara Hospital on the Gold Coast. The infectious diseases specialist at Pindara, John Gerrard, had helped treat a case of Lemierre's Syndrome fifteen years earlier when at Royal Prince Alfred Hospital in Sydney. From talking with Kobe and examining Kristin he immediately diagnosed Lemierre's. Someone upstairs, it seemed, was looking after our Kristin.

Kristin was moved to the intensive care ward at the Gold Coast Hospital. The intensivist there, Hugh Thomas, had never treated Lemierre's Syndrome, but had witnessed a case when he was an intern in South Africa. Miracles never cease—further treatment for glandular fever would almost certainly have been fatal.

Kristin spent her eighteenth birthday in a drug-induced coma. Lemierre's Syndrome caused a septic blood clot to form and spread to her lungs, which developed into pneumonia—this turned out to be the less horrible of two awful options. It was fortunate that the clot which had formed in Kristin's jugular vein headed south; it was dangerously close to her brain, and it was feared that it would touch her brain and cause a massive stroke. It was surreal; this was Kristin's eighteenth birthday and she was fighting for her life. How could this possibly be?

I was in the waiting room when my phone rang. It was Dave Tice.

'Thanks for calling, mate. What's up?'

'I'm at the hospital,' Dave replied.

'What hospital?'

'I'm at Royal Prince Alfred in Sydney. Nick got knocked off his bike; he's in a bad way.' Fuck, what else could go wrong?

Nick was Dave and Lesley's eldest boy. He was riding his bike when he was taken out by a turning supermarket truck, and went under the wheels. The accident was close to their home and Dave got there and tried to do what he could. Nick's right leg had been 'de-gloved'—that is, the skin on his upper leg had been detached and stripped away. Or, in Dave's words, his skin had been 'pushed down like a footy sock' around Nick's ankle. Thankfully, he'd be okay. Sore as hell, but okay.

With Kristin still in the intensive care unit, I was back and forth between the Gold Coast and Sydney. It was all a blur, an unbelievable situation, unearthly. When I returned to the hospital after forty-eight hours in Sydney I saw another person in Kristin's bed: a huge, bloated, discoloured person that was clearly not long for this earth. What the hell had happened? Where was Kristin? My mind went into overdrive and, fearing the absolute worst, I panicked. The nurses explained that it was Kristin I was looking at. It was shocking, a sight I'll never forget. Strangely, it made the situation more bearable—I felt as though I was waiting for Kristin to return and take the place of this unfamiliar shape in the bed. That said a lot about my state of mind.

Kristin's lungs were 'hard', basically locked with fluid, and her vital organs were starting to shut down, one by one. The decision was then made to get her into surgery in an attempt to drain the fluid from her lungs. The doctors were fearful of even moving her, but really they had no choice. A helicopter was on standby to take her north to Brisbane should things go awry. Could it get any worse? The doctors didn't want to move her at all but they were prepared to put her into a helicopter, which had just landed on the hospital roof. Shit, no, please—she'd just turned eighteen.

Over a litre of fluid was drained from each of Kristin's lungs and, fortunately, the fluid showed no signs of infection. Kristin went back to the ICU and, thankfully, the chopper wasn't needed. We were advised that nothing more could be done other than continuing with her regime of massive doses of antibiotics, while she remained on life support. Slowly she began to rally, although she was still reliant on life support. When Kristin started to produce a tiny amount of urine, it was a small but positive sign that her body was starting to function again.

Peter Steele, Kristin's grandfather, put things in perspective.

'Never has such a small bag of pee made so many people so happy.'

Kristin pulled through and got on with her life. She was amazing, an inspiration. Our beautiful, fun-loving Kristin was back. I was certain from that point, as no doubt she was too, that she'd now enjoy life to the fullest. It was impossible for me to be prouder; here was this stunning person with a wonderful, warm soul and a huge conscience, wise beyond her years. I felt that the illness added an extra facet to her character. She went to work at the Hard Rock Café, finished her studies, travelled. It was with much optimism, hope and some tears that we saw her off at Sydney Airport, headed for London via Japan and her future.

I learned a huge lesson from Kristin: she beat the odds and came out the other side, dusted herself off and attacked life with a passion. Why waste a day, even a moment? Made sense to me.

ϟ

When I was a kid you were either a Beatles or a Stones fan—and I was definitely a Stones man. The Stones were my band right from the first time I heard 'Not Fade Away' on the radio. It could have been their strong blues influence that got me, although I did like the 'bad boy' image, too.

My first clumsy attempts at putting together bands always involved plenty of Stones tunes. In fact, I'm still playing a few of them now in the acoustic thing I do with Dave: 'Little Red Rooster', 'Not Fade Away' and 'Under My Thumb' all feature in our current set. It was a pleasant surprise to find a few Stones tunes in the AC/DC set list when I joined in 1975; they may have disappeared very soon after I joined but the influence remained.

Fast-forward almost thirty years and it was with some serious anticipation that I headed to the Enmore Theatre in Sydney on 20 February 2003 with Dave Tice, Graham Kennedy and Bille to see the Stones play on their 40 Licks tour. The Enmore's only a 1500-seater; a cool little venue, perfect to see a great band such as the Stones. It's a real old-time theatre, with a sloping floor, small stage, and all the atmosphere that comes with seeing a band from close range—it's like a step back in time in this age of concrete bunkers and superdomes.

As we got near the venue, I couldn't help but think of that night in London, in May 1976, when we went off to see the Stones play at Earls Court. We'd scored some passes from Atlantic. Michael Browning came along too, and we must have been pumped, because he mentioned, as we walked to the gig, that he didn't realise we could all walk so bloody fast. And there was a bit of excitement in the air, not that any of us would have admitted it—we were way too cool for that, and I felt that the other guys might have scoffed at any over-the-top comment from me. I kept things in check and kept walking—fast. Angus, however, wasn't with us.

'Why would I want to go?' he grumbled back at the band house. 'I'm not interested.'

I didn't really care; I was psyched.

That 1976 show opened up with a flourish. The lights went down and the incredibly pompous 'Fanfare for the Common Man' filled the air. The stage was this massive cone shape. The band stood in the middle of the cone and the sides opened up like huge petals on a hydraulic flower. It was all very grand but to me it seemed overblown. I felt it had fuck-all to do with rock and roll. They started their set proper with 'Honky Tonk

Women' and then they went into much of the *Black and Blue* album, their latest. This was their first tour with Ron Wood, formerly of the Faces, on guitar.

The record has some funky stuff on it; to me it was a real departure from traditional Stones fare and not to my taste. I couldn't really see it appealing to the other guys in AC/DC, either. I know I was disappointed; I stood there thinking to myself that if this is what the 'Greatest Rock Band in the World' was serving up, then we weren't too far off. We could really crack this thing. I mean, if this was the Stones' best, why not us?

So almost thirty years later I was off to Enmore to see the Stones once again, now one of rock's last true survivors. I downed a couple of Scotches in the nearby pub before the show, so I was good to go. I was at the other end of a strange few weeks and seriously needed a big night out to brighten things up.

I'd been out of AC/DC for many a long year by now, but tried to keep up to date with their activities. They were due to be inducted into the Rock and Roll Hall of Fame, and not before time. I assumed that the current line-up, plus Bon, would make the cut, and this made perfect sense to me. But I was pleasantly surprised when word started filtering back to me that I would also be included. Actually I was floored when journalist, author and friend Murray Engleheart called to tell me that the Hall of Fame website mentioned that I was in. Murray had a better idea than most of my relationship with the band, or should I say lack of relationship. There was nothing there at all. Our last interaction had been strictly legal, drawn out, and had put a full stop to everything.

'I can't fucking believe it,' I said to Murray.

'The ice may have thawed,' he replied.

Bloody unlikely, I thought, but what the hell—the Rock and Roll Hall of Fame sounded pretty thrilling to me. I was always proud of my work with the band, despite our falling out, and this would be a huge rap.

But my initial instinct was to let the Hall of Fame people know that I would decline the nomination, even though it was hugely appreciated. I figured that was the dignified way to go. I couldn't see me being welcomed with open arms by the band, given our recent past. Many of my cohorts in the business congratulated me but also said, 'Wait and see what happens.' Pleasantly surprised but cautious was the best way to sum up the general reaction from those I knew.

In the end I decided to sit it out and see what happened, going against my gut instinct to knock it back. I was almost certain a curve ball would appear from somewhere. Still, I have to be honest, I did hold out some hope that the dust had settled and there might just be a chance of everyone, me included, smiling for the cameras and then moving on. Roly McAdam, my good friend and adviser throughout this period, put forward the thought that surely the Hall of Fame would have cleared the list of nominees with the band, but with the disclaimer that it was only a nomination. Roly was in contact with Suzanne Evans from the Hall of Fame—so why not find out?

At first, the Hall of Fame was full of positive signs: I was given dates, details of the induction at the Waldorf Astoria, the arrangements to be made. They said they'd be in contact and get the information to me. But then the temperature turned chilly. Roly's calls weren't being returned after the first week—was this the curve ball I'd been predicting? Sure as fuck was.

When we did get a reply, it was simply to announce that the Hall of Fame had seen fit to review the nomination and had come to the conclusion that I didn't qualify. I was out.

'Okay then, if that's the case that's fine,' said Roly. 'Where do we find the criteria?' No one was able to point Roly in the direction of the criteria they'd based their decision on. I have always wondered what triggered that review. Still do.

Let me just say that the band richly deserved to be in the Hall of Fame. It was way overdue. Bon had to be included, of course, as well as the current line-up. And I had absolutely no problem with not being included; in the AC/DC timeline I was there for only a brief time—an important time in my opinion, but a heartbeat by comparison with Cliff's thirty-year-plus tenure. What I found galling was the Hall of Fame's attitude. If a mistake was made, fine, then they should have dealt with it. A simple apology or at least an explanation would have been appreciated.

So, yeah, I was coming out the other end of a very strange time when we went to see the Stones play the Enmore. Tonight, the only important thing to me was that they opened with 'Midnight Rambler', then ripped straight into 'Tumblin' Dice'. That was as good as it gets. As they say, the joint was rockin'.

Being a long-time Stones fan, it was great to hear a lot of the old stuff, tunes that I'd butchered in my early attempts to put a band together, and had handled a bit better during my early days with AC/DC. Then, boom! I was jolted back into the present day. Mal and Angus stepped onto the stage with the Stones for a spirited version of 'Rock Me Baby'. Got to say I turned a tad green, but it was a wonderful moment. My two old bandmates, a pair of hard-to-read characters but truly top-shelf musicians, up there playing with the seemingly unstoppable Rolling Stones—the same band Angus decided not to see way back in Earls Court. What made it more poignant for me was the Hall of Fame shambles. Looking on, I couldn't help but wonder, 'What the fuck happened here?'

I'm not sure I'll ever know the full story, but for these few minutes, in this great venue, with my wife and my buddies, watching my old bandmates doing their thing with Mick, Keith and the rest of them, well, I couldn't help but be impressed. My life had taken some odd turns, and I had my share of regrets, but tonight it felt really good to be in this room, hearing these timeless songs.

My fiftieth birthday party fell on a Saturday, 4 March 2006, the same day as a regular Tice & Evans gig at our new spiritual home, the Sandringham Hotel in Newtown. We were hosting the party at our place in Lilyfield, but being an old trooper, I couldn't blow out a gig, so I did the first set and got my good pal Ian Miller to cover for the second. I had a bunch of people coming from Melbourne and I wanted to be home to welcome them.

But I couldn't get a cab. It was getting on and I was starting to worry when I spotted one parked a hundred metres down the road. The driver must have been getting a burger, I figured. I trotted down the road, got in the front seat, and was surprised to see the driver behind the wheel and a young lady in the back. I started apologising profusely but then—hey, wait a minute. It was my sister Judy. She'd planned to surprise me, having flown up with a good pal, Dean Barclay. They'd stopped to pick up another friend when I jumped in their cab. Not bad in a city of almost five million people. Judy's surprise went up in smoke but what a great start to the night—and we were going to the same party anyway, so I saved on the cab fare.

The usual suspects, around 120 of them, had been rounded up, including my girls Bille and Virginia (Kristin was in Europe), as well as Graham Kennedy, his wife Josette and their son Tobi, along with most of my crew from Melbourne, which included my mother Norma and my second mother Rose Kennedy, Graham's mum. Dave Tice, Mick Cocks, Brian Todd and Owen Orford, the former singer from Contraband (the bloke Bon thought was a 'ripper of a singer') were there, too. The boys from the East Sydney Bulldogs rolled up, and they could make the back garden look crowded just on their own. We had a PA set up for music and also a nice selection of Gibson acoustics for anyone who fancied a play. We were all ready for a big one.

I'd made two important decisions prior to the night. The first was that I'd gut it up and instead of using the Carlton Football Club song I'd stare down my phobia and let the assembled freeloaders sing me 'Happy Birthday'. I'd also decided to get a tattoo on my chest: B K V, my girls' initials. But confronting one phobia at a time was enough; for now I'd endure 'Happy Birthday' as a cleanskin.

The Scotch and Cokes and assorted party favours were being ingested and working their magic as I neared my moment of fate. I'd dodged it at my twenty-first in London with AC/DC, but there was no way out this time. I was summoned to the lawn for the 'official' part of proceedings. Bille thanked everyone for coming and I was starting to feel that a tattoo would have been the easier option.

Bille continued: 'I've arranged a present for Mark from London.'

'Cool,' I thought, 'another guitar.'

We have a back gate that leads to the house of our neighbour, Chris Turner. Coincidentally Chris was a guitar player in Buffalo with Dave and a perennial stand-by/stand-in guitarist with Rose Tattoo. It's Chris's fingers that feature on the original Australian cover of the *Let There Be Rock* LP.

I was still none the wiser when Kristin walked through our back gate. It was the last thing I was expecting and it took a moment or two for me to grasp exactly what was going on. I was stunned. I hadn't seen Kristin for the eighteen months she was living in London. What seemed to all the freeloaders like a long three-way hug with my two beautiful daughters masked (or at least I think it masked) the fact that I was in pieces. What a wonderful moment, but yet so odd—I was as happy as Larry yet I was crying. I was completely rattled. It was like we were the only three people in the world; nobody else existed at that moment. It was without doubt my favourite hug of all time, one that I will cherish for the rest of my days. I've always believed there is some special dynamic about father/daughter relationships.

My head finally cleared. I realised that Kristin was valiantly trying to introduce to me her boyfriend, Chris Nicholson, who'd accompanied her on the trip and who I'd not even noticed. When I took the time to acknowledge his existence, I found that Chris was a strikingly tall young man from Trondheim, Norway, born to an English academic father and a Norwegian mother.

'I believe you like Glenfiddich,' were Chris's first words to me, as he handed me a litre bottle of the fine single malt. 'Happy birthday, Mark.'

I thanked him and turned to Kristin. 'I love him already!'

What was set to be a big night just got a whole lot bigger.

My wife Bille had plotted to get Kristin and Chris over from London for the occasion and kept it a secret for months. I'd spoken to Kristin a few days before the party and she'd kept the charade going beautifully. To sneak Kristin into the country for my fiftieth was the most unbelievably kind, warm and thoughtful gesture. To say that I will be forever thankful just doesn't seem adequate.

For the record, I have absolutely no recollection of hearing 'Happy Birthday'. I've been told it was sung with gusto.

What brought me crashing back to earth was the world's greatest hangover, which greeted me some time the next day. I say some time as I have no idea when I stirred from my alcohol-induced coma, but I do know what woke me: the nastiest headache of all time. If there was a headache Olympics, this one was the gold medallist. No way I was scaring this off at the bottom of a swimming pool, like I did back in 1977 in Perth. Too many risks. I was no spring chicken anymore. I was fifty. Fuck, fifty years old—how did that happen?

The next few days were spent recuperating and spending some blissful time with Kristin and getting to know Chris. Kristin and Chris went scooting around Sydney with Virginia riding shotgun—she was not letting her big sister out of her sight. Life was good at Lilyfield; if this was as good as it got, I thought to myself, it'd do me nicely. And if the Big Fella could see his way clear to ease the hangovers back a notch or two, that would also be lovely.

After a bit we waved goodbye to Kristin as she and Chris set off on a road trip up the east coast to a family home at Mission Beach, Queensland. The wonderful surprise visit was over but I couldn't have wished for more. To be with Kristin and to see that she and Chris were so happy together was perfect, absolutely perfect.

Business-wise, the guitar hunting at Downtown Music was coming along nicely. The occasional 1960 Les Paul Standard or early sixties Custom Colour Fender Stratocaster would find its way into our hands, which was always guaranteed to bring a big smile to the faces of a couple of guitar nuts like Carlo and myself. And Dave and I were cruising along with our duo, gigging all over the country.

Our acoustic blues-based duo had morphed into a hard-edged format, featuring not only Dave's great voice but a whole load of original tunes and quite a bit of between-song shenanigans. I embraced it as my personal mission to try to break Dave up during and between songs. We took our work seriously but were also very serious about enjoying ourselves and taking the punters along for the ride.

Life had a rhythm; it was ticking along. I could have used some spare time for golf but I knew there'd be plenty of chances for that later. Ginnie was growing up quickly, a beautiful little soul, making loads of new friends at Annandale North Public. Kristin was there for her first day at school, along with her Nana Norma, which made that typically tough step a whole lot easier.

Kristin and Chris went back to Amsterdam, where they now lived. She was working at the Hard Rock Café, with a likely career beckoning in theatre set design, costume design, a career in which she could use her flamboyance. She worked as a DJ, too. During a gig in Oslo, Norway, she wore a dress made out of balloons, in Betty Page style. She would strategically pop balloons after songs, until all that was left was a few strips of well-placed gaffa tape. I *saw* the photos. As her dad, I'm still trying to process that one.

Just after 3 am on 6 June 2007, Bille and I were woken by the phone. 'Something's up,' I thought. Bille's mother Virginia, Ginnie's namesake, hadn't been the best. But Bille handed me the phone.

It was Kobe.

'Mark, Kristin's dead.'

'Sorry?'

Silence.

With my mind reeling, Kobe told me what had happened. Kristin was running late for work at the Hard Rock Café; she was due to start at 10 am. She was riding her pink mountain bike and had stopped on a corner on Overtoom, one of Amsterdam's busiest streets, to call and let them know she'd be there soon. A massive cement mixer truck cut the corner, hit Kristin, dragging her between the sets of dual wheels. She died at the scene.

I listened as Kobe's voice trailed off. I felt something click inside me; it was weird, there was no 'this can't be happening' or 'it must be a dream'. I knew Kristin was gone. I felt it. Everything stopped, everything, there was only one word coming out of me. 'No. No.'

'Kobe,' I asked. 'Do you have someone with you?' ('Please don't let her be alone,' I thought.)

'Dad's here.'

'Let me talk to him, please.'

I asked Peter about what I already knew was fact. There was no chance of a mistake, I was certain of that. I knew she'd left us. Peter advised me they'd spoken to the police in Amsterdam and the local police were on their way over to Kobe's house to do whatever they had to do. There was nothing to say. What could I say? I had to get off this phone. I hated this fucking phone.

'I'll call back soon,' I said. That's all I had in me.

I went downstairs, only to have the kitchen floor rush up and hit me in the face.

Soon after, Bille and I were sitting together in the family room, totally shattered. How could this be? How could Kristin not be with us? Kobe and Kristin were as close as a mother and daughter could possibly be, they were best friends, brought even closer by Kristin's illness. Kristin had made it through all that crap only for this to happen?

It was still the middle of the night. We decided the next person that had to be told was Virginia. We decided to let her sleep as normal till 7 am and then we'd tell her. But how? How do you tell a ten-year-old girl that her big sister has been killed? We sat quietly, waiting. We were sitting there in utter disbelief, distraught, destroyed. Life as we loved it was over. What was the point? This word kept flashing in my mind: 'Why?' Everything was so damn quiet. Still. Desolate.

Seven am ticked closer. Then the dreaded alarm went off and we went into Virginia's room and sat on her bed as she awoke.

'Virginia,' I said quietly. 'Wake up, sweetheart. There's been a terrible accident.'

Kobe and Peter Steele flew to Amsterdam almost immediately to take care of arrangements and to be with Chris. Bille, Virginia, Graham Kennedy and I met them in transit at Sydney Airport. It's impossible to put into words how I felt on seeing Kobe. She was unbelievably brave but broken, absolutely devastated.

The following days passed in a blur as friends and family gathered around, giving us strength. Graham, Dave and Lesley Tice never left our sides. Our door was open to all; you just cannot underestimate the power of friendship and warmth. I was learning how caring, kind and supportive people could be. You know when you speak with someone who is suffering a loss, and you hug them, tell them you're sorry for their loss, and feel that it hasn't helped one bit? I'm here to tell you it helps like you wouldn't believe. To know people care and that you're not alone is a real comfort. I needed every last scrap of it right now.

It's my belief that you see the true character of a person in times of adversity and I'm blessed to have so many friends that came through for me—for us. John Swan and Jim Barnes were constantly in touch, checking in, when they were also trying to deal with losing their father, Big Jim. That's a show of true friendship I'll never forget.

My grief was indescribable; it cut so deep. My own sense of loss was making me feel selfish, guilty. I was numb, in shock. While it would have been easy to disappear in my own grief, what about Kristin? She'd lost everything—her future with Chris, *her life*. How do you come to terms with that?

Peter Steele called and told me the decision had been made to have Kristin's funeral in Amsterdam, so I was on the next plane. The solitude of the twenty-two-hour Qantas flight was a blessing in disguise; it gave me time to gather my thoughts and think of Kristin. Good memories were trying to break through my awful fog. I was relieved to be sitting in a row of three seats by myself. I must have looked terrible, because one of the flight crew asked if she could sit down.

'Is there something wrong, Mr Evans? Can I help?'

I explained why I was on my way to Amsterdam. I thought I'd held it together as best I could and turned to look at my new friend, who had tears rolling down her cheeks.

'I'm so sorry, Mr Evans.'

She went down to the back of the plane, where I guess she filled in the rest of the crew. She returned and put her hand on my shoulder.

'Can I get you anything, Mr Evans?'

'Scotch and Coke,' was my answer. But my first instinct was to say, simply: 'Kristin.'

I had a six-hour layover in London before the flight into Amsterdam. The Qantas flight crew had kindly arranged for me to freshen up and take it easy in the British Airways first-class lounge at Heathrow. I was sitting in a very plush club chair trying to read a newspaper.

'Tea, sir?' someone asked.

'No, I'm fine, thanks,' came the reply.

I knew that voice. I lowered my London *Times* to see Clive James's face looking straight at me over the top of *his* London *Times*. I'd always wanted to meet Clive James, but just not now, please. I knew his story well from his wonderful autobiographies; he was raised in Kogarah, Sydney.

'It's a long way from Kogarah, Clive,' I offered.

'Quite correct, well observed,' Clive parried.

We both went back to the *Times* but I thought I might as well try to start a conversation. Okay, what do we have in common? That's it—we both have two daughters. Had. Shit.

I needed to stretch my legs and ended up in an airport souvenir shop and decided to pick up a few little things for Ginnie and her friends. I rustled up some fridge magnets, pencils and a couple of tiny red double-decker London buses. You couldn't go anywhere at Heathrow at the time without the sweet, open, innocent face of three-year-old Madeline McCann staring up at you. She'd gone missing in Portugal the month before.

The middle-aged female shop assistant was filling up paper bags with my knick-knacks—Madeline's face was also on the brown papers bags. I was studying young Madeline's face intently, when the shop assistant spoke to me.

'Awful business that. Can you possibly imagine what it would be like to lose your daughter.'

I wanted the ground to open up and swallow me. I wanted this nightmare to end, right now.

'I should loathe Amsterdam,' I thought to myself, as I crossed a bridge over a canal on my way to my hotel from Central, Amsterdam's main railway station. I should fucking hate this city; it took Kristin away from me. But within minutes I was seeing why Kristin loved the place. It was beautiful, calm but vital and worldly at the same time, with buildings straight out of fairytales, and so many people on bicycles. I'd been to Amsterdam before but it had melted into so many other European cities on my AC/DC itinerary. Not any more.

My heart sunk when I thought of my earlier plans to visit Kristin and Chris, which had gone awry. It would have been idyllic. I stopped on the bridge to take in the sights. The brightly painted barges plied the canal and one elderly, white-bearded barge captain waved happily to me. I waved back. It struck me how quickly life can change; everything around you continues on while your world has been obliterated.

After Kristin's funeral a wake was held at one of her favourite places, the Filmmuseum Amsterdam. The Filmmuseum is the Netherlands' national centre for cinematography, housed in a massive old villa in the picturesque Vondelpark. It's a stunning setting. Kristin's friends organised the wake, and I got the sense that the city must have started to feel like home for her, with so many Dutch friends. I was beginning to believe that Kristin was at the happiest point of her life, with Chris, in Amsterdam. It was comforting to meet and spend time with these fine people, but they were too young to be going through such a thing. We all were. I looked around the stone-walled café, full of cigarette smoke, wine bottles and a seemingly endless supply of yapping dogs. Only Kristin was missing.

I welcomed the solitude of the long flight back to Sydney. It gave me time to reflect, to try to—try to what? Kristin was gone; was anything going to be right again?

Time passes, first hour by hour, then days and months slip by and you endure, you find a way to continue. Those awful, sad-arsed clichés popped up with some regularity: 'You have to move on.' 'Time heals all wounds.' But you know what?

People who spout that crap don't get it. What I've found is that the pain never leaves but you become better at adapting, allowing for it, recognising it for what it is. The sadness, grief and pain that I felt so deeply was natural. If it wasn't there, wouldn't that mean I didn't care? The beautiful memories of funny stories and good times started to come more easily to me, and I began to learn. I learned who I really was, and learned that I have family and friends who have qualities that I could only wish for. When the sadness descended on me, as it often would and still does, I thought of the good times and just how Kristin would have wanted us to continue, to live our lives to the fullest.

I miss Kristin beyond belief, beyond any words. I see things that remind me of her and they always bring a smile to my face: green velvet Doc Martens, grilled bacon and cheese on toast, postcards from Disneyland, chocolate, Faster Pussycat, chip-eating birds, Betty Page, fishing for yabbies. All of these and more are guaranteed to brighten my day; it feels like Kristin is sending me little messages. Keep moving. Enjoy life. Never give up.

Acknowledgements

Writing a memoir is a solitary task but it is impossible to turn it all into a book without having the support, advice and expertise of a crew of professionals who 'get it'. I have always been fortunate that the right people seem to appear in my life precisely when they should and with Jeff Apter that is exactly what happened. Jeff is the guy who put my words through his writing wringer; a tireless mentor, full of good humour and sage advice, and brilliant to work with. My thanks go out to Jeff for helping make writing *Dirty Deeds* an incredible journey and, yes mate, 'It's cheaper than a psychiatrist.'

I would also like to thank my favourite literary agent in the whole wide world, Pippa Masson of Curtis Brown, a delight to work with—I'm so very glad to have Pippa on my side of the table; Jane Palfreyman, Lauren Finger, Elizabeth Cowell and Kate Hyde at Allen & Unwin for all the continued effort, support and enthusiasm; and Peter FitzSimons for pointing me in the right direction at the outset and giving me a damn good shove.

Thanks to the cast and crew who have travelled the road with me so far, most importantly my most wonderful family. Bille, Kristin and Ginnie, thank you for being exactly who you are, absolute treasures.

Finally, thanks to all the punters who have said 'You should write a book' and have shown me so much support over the years, some of who have become firm friends—Aaron Baker, Dr Sharon Dawood, Dr Volker Janssen, Doug Thorncroft.

It's a long way . . .

Mark Evans was born in Melbourne, Australia. He is a musician, vintage guitar trader and now author, *Dirty Deeds* being his first book. Mark was the bass player in the Bon Scott led AC/DC, gigging, touring, carousing and recording the albums *TNT*, *Dirty Deeds Done Dirt Cheap* and *Let There Be Rock*. Mark lives in Sydney, Australia, with his wife Bille and daughter Virginia, and is one part of the acoustic blues/roots duo ingeniously branded 'Dave Tice and Mark Evans' with singer and long-time friend Dave Tice.

www.markevansblues.com
www.ticeandevans.com
www.facebook.com/ticeandevans
www.reverbnation.com/ticeandevans

In a career spanning twenty years, **Jeff Apter** has written more than a dozen works of non-fiction, including bestselling biographies of the Finn brothers (*Together Alone*) and former test cricketer Michael Slater (*Slats*). His other subjects have included Jeff Buckley, Keith Urban and the Red Hot Chili Peppers. He spent five years as Music Editor at Australian *Rolling Stone* and is the Music Contributor for Australian *Vogue*. Jeff is currently co-authoring a Kasey Chambers biography and also working on *Shooting Star: The Marc Hunter Story*, both of which will be published in 2011. He lives on the New South Wales south coast, sharing his life with his two children, Elizabeth and Christian, his wife, Diana, and a hefty record collection.

www.jeffapter.com.au